# Stained and Painted

# HERALDIC GLASS

## Burrell Collection

### British and Selected Foreign Armorial Panels

THE CORPORATION OF THE CITY OF GLASGOW
GLASGOW ART GALLERY AND MUSEUM
1962

# FOREWORD

This year, from September 8th to 14th, Edinburgh will be host to the Sixth International Congress of Genealogy and Heraldry. On the initiative of the Secretary to the Congress, it was decided to use this occasion for a special display of the Heraldic Stained Glass in which The Burrell Collection is so rich. The Museums and Art Galleries Committee of the Corporation endorsed the suggestion and Mr. William Wells, Keeper of the Collection, has arranged the exhibition and has written this catalogue. These are formidable tasks calling for specialised display on the one hand and detailed research on the other. We hope that the reward will be a wider general interest in both the historical and artistic aspects of a fascinating subject besides providing a feast of colour for all our visitors.

Thanks are due to David Reid of Robertland for the suggestion that Glasgow should show the Burrell heraldic glass, also for advice on books and help in identifying Nos. 11 and 62 in the catalogue. Among others who gave assistance were Mr. Arthur Lane and Mr. John Lowe of the Victoria and Albert Museum, Mr. Revel Oddy of the Royal Scottish Museum, Mr. C. S. Ralegh Radford of Devon, Major D. C. W. Peyton of Surrey, the Rev. G. E. Raven of Canterbury and the Rev. J. B. Goodchild of Isleham, Cambridgeshire, Mrs. Winifred E. Thomas of London, Miss Elisabeth Prins of The Hague, Professor Hans Wentzel of Stuttgart, Mr. Lawrence Tanner of Westminster Abbey, Dr. Peter Newton of the Barber Institute, Birmingham and Mr. D. G. King of Norwich.

The photographs for this catalogue, both in colour and in black and white, were taken by the Burrell Collection photographer, Miss Flora Ritchie, and other members of the staff have worked hard in support of the Keeper. The display cases were built and the lighting installed by our Museum Staff under the direction of Mr. James Black, the Clerk of Works.

S. M. K. HENDERSON, *Director.*

# INTRODUCTION

Of the five hundred and eighty-seven windows and panels of stained glass acquired by Sir William and Lady Burrell and now forming part of the Burrell Collection, over half are heraldic, and a number of others, though not exclusively heraldic, are of some heraldic interest. Some of these have been included in this catalogue although they could equally well appear in a catalogue of figure subjects.

The collection seems to have been chiefly formed from about 1920 onwards. In 1944 when the gift was made, two hundred and forty-three panels of religious and heraldic glass were in the windows of Sir William's house near Berwick-on-Tweed, Hutton Castle. A few of these were removed in 1948 for a special exhibition in Glasgow, but the majority remained there until 1956 when all were taken out and transferred to Glasgow with the exception of those in the bedrooms and sitting rooms still in use and these were not transferred until March, 1962, about nine months after the death of Lady Burrell.

In addition to the glass in the windows at Hutton Castle, there was a quantity of stained glass in store there. Moreover, Sir William added considerably to the Collection after 1944 and the purchases he made between this date and that of his death in March, 1958, included some of the most impressive of the heraldic glass— the series from Vale Royal acquired in 1947 and the even larger and more homogeneous series from Fawsley Hall in 1950.

The basis of the present catalogue is a typescript inventory. Like the inventories which exist for other parts of the Collection this was probably drawn up primarily for insurance purposes, but unlike them it contains, or part of it contains, considerably more information than they usually do. This at least applies to the first two hundred and forty-three entries which is a room to room list of the stained glass as set up in the windows of Hutton Castle, not only in the living rooms, but in the bedrooms, servants' quarters, and even the bathrooms. Most of the heraldic glass in this section of the inventory is quite copiously described and annotated, but is disappointingly reticent as to the date when each piece was acquired and where it came from, and it was presumably drawn up at a time when this information had already been forgotten, or maybe there still remained reasons for suppressing it. There is nothing to indicate the authorship of the document of which the inventory is a typed and perhaps partly incomplete version, but there can be no doubt that the information derives from Mr. Wilfred Drake, from whom, either on his own or in partnership with Mr. Grosvenor Thomas, most of the glass was purchased. The glass listed as in store at Hutton Castle is very briefly itemised. The subsequent entries for glass purchased after 1944 are again fuller and always record the date and the name of the dealer, but frequently omit the name of the house from which the glass derived. All in all the inventory may be described as a comparatively lavish but haphazard and erratic source of information.

The half-tone illustrations reproduced here show the glass as arranged for the exhibition of heraldic art in the Burrell Collection displayed in the Glasgow Art Gallery during August and September, 1962. For this purpose the glass was mounted in twenty-four artifically lighted cases represented in this catalogue by the forty-eight black and white reproductions each of which shows half a case. With some exceptions, the arrangement is according to country of origin, the British being followed by the Flemish, German, Swiss and Dutch. The arrangement of the British glass is for the most part according to date, but this has been waived where a rigid adherence to chronology conflicted with some other consideration. Wherever possible, for example, glass from the same house, though of varying date, has been kept together as a series.

Outstanding among the latter is the series of forty shields from the banqueting hall at Fawsley Hall, near Daventry in Northamptonshire, the residence of the ancient family of Knightley from 1416, until the death of Rainald, Baron Knightley of Fawsley in 1895, when the estate was inherited by his cousin, Lord Gage, whose mother was a Knightley. In so far as the stained glass is concerned the key-figure in this pedigree is Sir Edmund Knightley, who is believed to have rebuilt the house at Fawsley between 1537 and 1542 (the year of his death) and to have embellished it with the armorial glass now in the Burrell Collection, among which his own shield with the Knightley quarterings impaling De Vere must have taken pride of place. His marriage with Ursula, sister and co-heiress of John Vere, Earl of Oxford, accounts for the presence in the house of the eight contemporary roundels commemorating the ancestry of his wife. His own ancestry is recorded in the more or less rectangular panels with hour-glass shaped shields set amidst foliage and other fertile decoration. A number of these are specifically concerned with his mother's maternal descent. His father, the third Knightley of Fawsley, had been made a Knight of the Bath when the future Henry VIII was created Duke of York, an honour which probably lends special significance to the four rectangular panels with royal arms and the cross of St. George. Also in the house were four ornate medallions, two of which bear the arms of Sir Edmund's brother and successor—Sir Valentine (died 1566), who married Anne Ferrers, and of his brother-in-law, Sir William Spencer of Althorp. These are both dated 1572 and were perhaps added by Sir Valentine's son, Sir Richard Knightley, who died in 1615 aged eighty-two, and whose arms and those of his wife, Mary Fermor, also figure in this part of the series, of which

the fourth is for Henry VIII and Jane Seymour (Sir Richard's second wife was a Seymour). Undated but perhaps also added by Sir Richard are the three garter medallions, one of which is certainly for William Parr, Earl of Essex, brother of Katherine Parr.

A few years earlier Sir William had acquired another series of hardly less interest, although it is typical of the erratic nature of the inventory that no certain indication is given there of the provenance of the thirty-seven medallions and panels it lists as having been acquired from Mr. Wilfred Drake in August, 1947. Whereas the Fawsley Hall series is very much centred in a single family, the Vale Royal one forms a county rather than a family unit, commemorating as it does a number of the landed gentry of Cheshire about the middle of the 16th Century. Some of these modest little armorial panels almost certainly came originally from Spurstow Hall where seven of them (Brereton, Brereton of Malpas, Ridley, Spurstow, Done, Kinderton, and Cholmondeley) were recorded by a contemporary antiquarian in 1599 (B. M. Harl. MS. 2151). Others probably come from Utkinton Hall, the home of the Done family, hereditary master Foresters of Delamere Forest. In 1755 the shields from both these houses were in the windows of Tarporley Rectory. It so happened that when the Reverend William Cole, friend of Horace Walpole and indefatigable recorder of antiquities, came to visit the Reverend John Allen, rector of Tarporley, he had the misfortune to break his leg as the result of a fall from his horse on the way. While convalescing in the house Cole made drawings with annotations of all the stained glass shields which were in the windows there. The drawings of the thirty-three panels made by Cole are now among the Cole manuscripts in the British Museum and of these eleven are now in the Burrell Collection (Minshull, Wilbraham, Holford, Done (2), Ridley, Ardern, Cholmondeley, Spurstow, Brereton of Malpas and Kinderton). Cole noted that while some of the shields were large and ancient " with Raies behind the Shield and the Name under " (he mistakenly attributed them to the 15th Century, half a century or more too early) others were comparatively small and modern (about the time of Charles II, which is probably about half a century too late). Two of the sesmall modern panels, one for Ardern and the other for John Done of Flaxyards and Utkinton who died in 1601 are among those in the Collection. (Whereas the earlier of these shields are in pot metal i.e. glass stained by mixing a variety of metallic oxides with the substance of the glass with the addition only of black enamel paint and a yellow pigment applied to the surface of the glass these later panels are wholly painted in translucent enamel pigments on white i.e. colourless glass).

After Mr. Allen's death in 1778, the Tarporley Rectory glass was apparently dismantled and a selection must have been acquired by the Cholmondeley family for Vale Royal, a mansion built after 1542 on the site of the ancient monastery. Here they joined a distinct series of armorial medallions, some for royalty, some for knights of the garter, which presumably were introduced into the house as an act of homage to the king and the leading nobility. Among them, however, were a few oval wreathed medallions for some of the most prominent Cheshire families (Booth, Venables, Brereton) which also figure in the humbler type of shields from Spurstow and Utkinton. All this glass remained at Vale Royal at least until 1922 when it was described by J. Paul Rylands and R. Stewart-Brown in two articles in The Genealogist (Vol. 38). A few of the panels recorded by Cole at Tarporley Rectory and now in the Burrell Collection were noted by the authors of these articles as " not at Vale Royal " and were presumably not accessible to them at the time. A few others also noted as " not at Vale Royal " were acquired for the Burrell Collection prior to 1944 and these may have been acquired by Drake from an unspecified source.

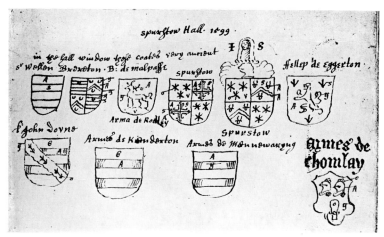

Spurstow Hall, 1599.
British Museum (Harl. MS. 2151, f. 167).

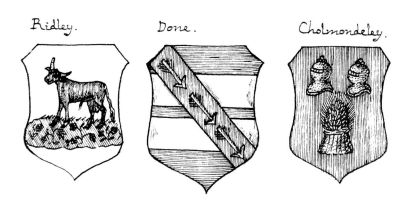

Tarporley Rectory, 1755.
British Museum (Add. MS. 5830, ink f. 42).

Done.

Tarporley Rectory, 1755.
British Museum (Add. MS. 5830, ink f. 40).

Arms of John Done. See Cat. No. 181.

# Catalogue

*(Quarterings not blazoned in the catalogue are given in the index)*

1 BEATRIX VAN VALKENBURG (d. 1277); daughter of Dirk II, Lord of Valkenburg (Limburg) and third wife of Richard, Earl of Cornwall, King of the Romans. She is kneeling and wears a mantle *(barry gules and sable)*. In the blue surround are a number of roundels charged with an Imperial Eagle, three of the upper roundels being partly obliterated by a white letter inscription: Beatrix de Valkenburch Regina Allemannie. Shaped panel; pot metal; some silver yellow stain (probably a replacement); 24 × 10½ in. Oxford School, late 13th Century. Probably from the Church of the Minorites, Oxford, where she was buried. Ex-Coll: George William Jerningham, 8th Baron Stafford of Costessey. Lit: M. Drake, The Costessey Collection, 1920, p. 19, No. 77; Apollo, 1935, (August), p. 80; The Antiquaries Journal, XVIII, 1938, pp. 142-5; Scottish Art Review, I, 4, 1947; C. Woodforde, English Stained and Painted Glass, 1954, p. 6. Original Gift; ex Hutton Castle, 1956. Inv. No. 88; Reg. No. 45.2.

It is not certain that the red and black bars on the mantle should be interpreted as a blazon. They are not the arms of either her father or her husband.

2 Roundel with shield of LISLE *(or on a chief azure three lions rampant of the first)* impaling STOURTON *(sable a bend or between six fountains)*; pot metal; dia. 13½ in. 15th Century. Original Gift; ex Hutton Castle, 1956. Inv. No. 33; Reg. No. 45.135. See no. 97 (Lisle).

3 Roundel with unnamed shield *(azure a saltire or)*, perhaps for ST. ALBAN'S ABBEY or town; pot metal; yellow stain in border (a replacement); dia. 8 in. 15th Century. Original Gift; ex Hutton Castle. Inv. No. 245; Reg. No. 45.69.

4 Shield of GARLAND, co. Lincs. *(gules two bars or in chief three besants)*; pot metal; 12½ × 10½ in. 15th Century. Acquired per Drake, 1947. Inv. No. 404; Reg. No. 45.170.

5 Panel with kneeling lady donor and shield of CHALONS, co. Devon *(gules two bars ermine between nine martlets argent)*; pot metal; abrasion; yellow stain; 17½ × 23⅞ in. 15th Century. Original Gift; ex Hutton Castle, 1956. Inv. No. 34; Reg. No. 45.39.

The panel appears to be composed of heterogeneous elements.

6 Panel with shield set in an ornamental canopied surround with two eagles and two lions *(Howard quartering Plantagenet and Delapole)*; pot metal; abrasion; yellow stain; 24¾×22 in. Norwich School, c. 1475. Ex. Coll: George William Jerningham, 8th Baron Stafford of Costessey. Lit: M. Drake, The Costessey Collection, 1920, p. 19, No. 77. Original Gift; ex Hutton Castle, 1956. Inv. No. 20; Reg. No. 45.131.

According to the inventory these are the arms of John Howard (1430-1485) 1st Duke of Norfolk the Yorkist leader, who was killed at Bosworth field in 1485 fighting for Richard III. He was descended by his mother, a Mowbray, from Thomas de Brotherton, Earl of Norfolk, second son of Edward I—hence the lions of England in the second and third quarters.

7 ROYAL TUDOR ARMS *(France and England quarterly)*, perhaps for Henry VII; pot metal; 12×10½ in. Late 15th Century. Original Gift, ex Hutton Castle, 1956. Inv. No. 32; Reg. No. 45.188.

The forepart of the bottom leopard in second quarter is restored with lion of later date.

8 Roundell with the shield of BEAUCHAMP *(gules, a fess between six martlets or)* as borne by various branches of the Beauchamp family; pot metal; yellow stain, (in the twisted border); dia. 11 in. 15th Century. Original Gift, ex Hutton Castle, 1956. Inv. No. 15; Reg. No. 45.130.

9 Panel with shield set in an ornamental surround similar to no. 6 *(De Vere quartering Howard and Chaucer)*; pot metal; abrasion; yellow stain; 24 × 22 in. Norwich School, c. 1475. Ex Coll: George William Stafford of Costessey. Lit: M. Drake, The Costessey Collection, 1920, p. 19, No. 78. Original Gift, ex Hutton Castle, 1956. Inv. No. 22; Reg. No. 45.132.

John de Vere (1442-1512-13), 13th Earl of Oxford, the Lancastrian leader at the Battle of Bosworth, was son of Elizabeth, daughter and heiress of Sir John Howard, grandfather of Sir John Howard, 1st Duke of Norfolk (see no. 6). They were therefore first cousins. He died at Hedingham Castle, for which it is supposed these two panels were made.

10 ROGER DE MORTIMER, 4th Earl of March and Ulster (d. 1397); shield
(*Mortimer quartering De Burgh*); pot metal; 10½×8½ in. 14th Century. Original
Gift; ex Hutton Castle, 1956. Inv. No. 90; Reg. 45.115. Compare B. M.
seal No. 11.969.

11 Quatrefoil with shield (*azure two swords in saltire points downwards*) suspended by
a strap from a tree, perhaps for SIR JOHN SCRYMGEOUR, Constable of Dundee
(d. c. 1460-61); pot metal, yellow stain; 13½×8 in. 15th Century. Acquired
per Adams-Acton, 1946; ex Hutton Castle, 1948. Inv. No. 439; Reg. No. 45.175.

Identified in Inventory as Bonar of Kimmerghame, but see Stevenson and Wood,
Scottish Heraldic Seals, p. 580.

12 Shield of CHAMPNEY (*argent, three bars nebuly gules*) impaling LECHECHE
(*chequy or and azure two bars gules*); pot metal; 10¾×9½ in. 14th Century. Original
Gift; ex Hutton Castle, 1956. Inv. No. 89; Reg. No. 45.114.

13 Shield (*gules, two lions passant guardant or*) perhaps for King JOHN before his
accession to the throne in 1199; pot metal; 9×7 in. 13th-14th Century. Lit:
Newton, Scottish Art Review, Vol. VIII, No. 4, 1962. Original Gift; ex Hutton
Castle, 1956. Inv. No. 110; Reg. No. 45.122.

Newton (op. cit.) points out that the same arms were used by King John's nephew,
Henry, Count Palatine of the Rhine, and his heirs, and an illegitimate son,
Richard de Varenne.

14 Barbed quatrefoil with the shield (*or, two lions passant in pale azure*) of SIR JOHN
DE SOMERY, of Dudley Castle, Worcs.; pot metal; 20½×17½ in. Early 14th
Century. Ex Coll: Bruce, sold Christie's 28. 6. 1935. Lit: Newton, Scottish
Art Review, Vol. VIII, No. 4, 1962. Original Gift; ex Hutton Castle, 1948.
Inv. No. 349; Reg. No. 45.109. (See colour repro. p. 5).

The barony of Dudley was held by the family of Somery from 1194 until 1322
when Sir John de Somery died.

15 Shield of CLARE, Earls of Hertford and Gloucester (*or three chevrons*); pot metal;
8½×6¾ in. 14th Century. Original Gift; ex Hutton Castle, 1956. Inv. No. 109;
Reg. No. 121.

16 Shield of NEVILLE *(gules a saltire argent)* impaling AUDLEY *(gules fretty or)*; pot metal!; 10½ × 9½ in. 14th Century. Acquired per Drake, 1948. Inv. No. 480; Reg. No. 45.287. (See colour repro. p. 12).

Ralph, 2nd Lord Neville married Alice, daughter of Hugh de Audley in 1326/7.

17 Roundel with shield *(gules, three lions passant guardant or, a label of three points azure)* perhaps for EDWARD II before his accession; pot metal; dia. 11 in. York School, 14th Century. ex Coll: Dr. Philip Nelson. Acquired per Drake, 1946; ex Hutton Castle, 1948. Inv. No. 421; Reg. No. 45.129.

18 Shield with the arms of NETTERVILL *(or a cross gules fretty argent)*; pot metal; 9½ × 7¾ in. 14th Century. Original Gift; ex Hutton Castle, 1956. Inv. No. 92, Reg. No. 45.116.

19 Shield of CHEDWORTH *(azure a chevron or between three wolf's heads erased of the last)* impaling GRAY *(vert a lion rampant within a bordure engrailed argent)*; pot metal; yellow stain; 8¼ × 7½ in. 15th Century. Original Gift (bought from Drake); ex Hutton Castle. Inv. No. 307; Reg. No. 45.168.

20 Panel with the shield of SIR JOHN DE HAUDLO in a barbed quatrefoil *(argent a lion rampant azure guttee d'or crowned or)*; pot metal; yellow stain; 17 × 18¼ in. 14th Century. Original Gift; ex Hutton Castle, 1956. Inv. No. 26; Reg. No. 45.111.

21 Shield *(azure a cross patonce between five martlets or)* perhaps for King EDWARD THE CONFESSOR; pot metal; silver yellow stain; 9 × 7 in. 15th Century. Acquired per Drake, 1948. Inv. No. 481; Reg. No. 45.176. (See colour repro. p. 12).

22 Shield of FITZHUGH *(azure, three chevrons braced, a chief or)*; pot metal; 8½ × 7¾ in. 14th Century. Ex Coll: Sir Hercules Read (Sold Sotheby's 9.11.1928, lot 716 as "from Tanfield Church, Yorks."). Exhib: B.F.A.C. (British Heraldic Art) 1916, p. 118, No. 2. Original Gift; ex Hutton Castle, 1956. Inv. No. 221; Reg. No. 45.124.

The chief is a modern replacement.

Cat. No. 16

Cat. No. 21

Cat. No. 27

Cat. No. 72

Cat. No. 80

Cat. No. 84

Cat. No. 85

Cat. No. 92

Cat. No. 104

23 Roundel with badge or crest *(an eagle displayed or)*; pot metal; dia. 6½ in. 14th Century. Ex Coll: Dr. Philip Nelson. Acquired per Drake, 1944. Inv. No. 406; Reg. No. 45.128.

Described in inventory as eagle badge of Edward III.

24 Shield of BLUNDEVILL *(quarterly per fess indented or and azure, a bend gules)*; pot metal; 8¾×7½ in. 14th Century. Original Gift; ex Hutton Castle, 1956. Inv. No. 220; Reg. No. 45.123.

25 Shield of NEVILLE *(azure a lion rampant or)*; pot metal; yellow stain; 9×7¼ in. 15th Century. Original Gift (bought from Drake); ex Hutton Castle. Inv. No. 300; Reg. No. 45.126.

26 Panel with shield of BEREFORD *(or three fleurs de lys sable)* in a barbed quatrefoil; pot metal; yellow stain; 16¾×18¾ in. 14th Century. Original Gift; ex Hutton Castle, 1956. Inv. No. 27; Reg. No. 45.112.

27 Shield of SIR JOHN DE RYVERS *(or masculy gules)*; pot metal; 11¼×8¼ in. Early 15th Century. Ex Coll: Dr. Philip Nelson. Acquired per Drake, 1946; ex Hutton Castle, 1948. Inv. No. 419; Reg. No. 173. (See colour repro. p. 12).

28 Shield of SULLIARD, co. Essex *(argent a chevron gules between three pheons sable)*; pot metal; 8¾×7¼ in. 15th Century. Original Gift; ex Hutton Castle, 1956; Inv. No. 121; Reg. No. 45.145.

29 Shaped shield of FORD, Abbey Field, co. Chester *(per fess or and ermine a lion rampant azure fretty argent and gules)*; pot metal; 18×9½ in. 16th Century. Original Gift; ex Hutton Castle, 1962. Inv. No. 64; Reg. No. 45.199.

30 Shield of DAVIES, co. Sussex *(argent a chevron sable between three spur revels gules)* impaling MORETON *(ermine a chief dancetty gules)*; pot metal; 8⅜×7¼ in. 15th Century. Original Gift; ex Hutton Castle, 1956. Inv. No. 122, Reg. No. 45.146.

31 Shield of BAZLEY *(azure three fleurs de lys argent)*; pot metal; 8½×7 in. 14th Century. Original Gift; ex Hutton Castle, 1962. Inv. No. 95; Reg. No. 45.117.

32 Barbed quatrefoil with shield of GLASTENBURY, co. Dorset *(or a bend fusilly sable)*; pot metal; 15×15 in. 14th Century. Original Gift; ex Hutton Castle, 1962. Inv. No. 53; Reg. No. 45.113.

33 Shield of MASSEY *(gules three fleurs de lys argent)*; pot metal; 8½×7 in. 14th Century. Original Gift; ex Hutton Castle, 1962. Inv. No. 96; Reg. No. 45.118.

34 Shield of STRINGER, Whiston Sharleston, Co. York *(sable, three eagles displayed erminois)*; yellow stain; 8¼×7½ in. 16th Century. Original Gift; ex Hutton Castle, 1962. Inv. No. 181; Reg. No. 45.217.

35 Shaped shield of GRIFFITH HAMPTON quartering HAYNES impaling CAVE; pot metal; 28×12 in. 16th Century. Original Gift; ex Hutton Castle, 1962. Inv. No. 65; Reg. No. 45.200.

According to the inventory, Anne Cave, wife of Griffith Hampton was the daughter of Antony Cave of Chicheley, co. Bucks., by Elizabeth, daughter of Thomas Lovet of Astwell.

36 Unnamed shield *(or an eagle displayed azure over all on a fess wavy argent three mullets sable)*; pot metal; 8½×7½ in. Probably Flemish, 16th Century. Original Gift; ex Hutton Castle, 1962. Inv. No. 182; Reg. No. 45.218.

37 Shield of CHALLERS, co. Cambridge *(argent a fess between three annulets gules)* quartering SERVINGTON *(ermine a chevron azure)*; pot metal; 10¾×10 in. 15th Century. Original Gift; ex. Hutton Castle, 1962. Inv. No. 175; Reg. No. 45.155.

38 Unnamed shield *(per fess gules and vert three hedgehogs proper)*; pot metal; dia. 12½ in. (mounted). 16th Century. Ex Coll: F. S. Eden; Hearst (New York). Original Gift; ex Hutton Castle. Inv. No. 297; Reg. No. 45.236.

39 Shield of BEAUMONT, Bretton, Co. York *(gules a lion rampant within an orle of crescents argent)*; pot metal ; 11×9 in. 15th Century. Original Gift; ex Hutton Castle, 1962. Inv. No. 177; Reg. No. 45.157.

40 SIR ROGER WENTWORTH of Codham Hall, Essex *(d. 1539)* and his wife ANNE TYRRELL *(d. 1534)* ; shaped shield: *(Dexter (1) and (4) Wentworth; (2) and (3) Howard; (5) Despencer; (6) Goushill; (7) Tibetot; (8) Badlesmere. Sinister: (1) Tyrrell; (2) Hellyon; (3) Rolfe; (4) Swynbourne; (5) Botetourt; (6) Gernon);* pot metal; abrasion; 14×12 in. 16th Century. Original Gift; ex Hutton Castle, 1962. Inv. No. 62; Reg. No. 45.197. See no. 42.

41 Roundel with the red rose of LANCASTER encircled by fragmentary garter motto and floral border; pot metal, yellow stain; dia. 15 in. 16th Century. Original Gift; ex Hutton Castle, 1962. Inv. No. 52; Reg. No. 45.191.

42 SIR JOHN WENTWORTH of Gosfield Hall, Essex *(d. 1567)* and his wife ANNE BETTENHAM *(d. 1575);* shaped shield *(Dexter: (1) and (10) Wentworth; (2) and (11) Despencer; (3) and (12) Howard; (4) and (7) Hellyon; (5) and (8) Swynbourne; (6) and (9) Botetourt. Sinister: Bettenham);* pot metal; abrasion; 14×12 in. 16th Century. Original Gift; ex Hutton Castle, 1962. Inv. No. 63; Reg. No. 45.198.

Sir John, eldest son of Sir Roger (see No. 40) was knighted in 1547. He and his wife, Anne, were buried in the Wentworth Chapel in Gosfield Church where their tomb bears an armorial shield of Wentworth, quarterly of fourteen, impaling Bettenham.

43 Shield of PAYNELL *(or two bars azure an orle of martlets sable within a bordure argent);* pot metal; yellow stain; 10¾×10 in. 16th Century. Original Gift; ex Hutton Castle, 1962. Inv. No. 174; Reg. No. 45.215.

44 Shield of HEATH *(argent, three ogresses, the first charged with a cross crosslet argent)* impaling KERVILLE *(gules a chevron or between three leopards' faces argent);* pot metal; abrasion; yellow stain; 7½×6½ in. 15th Century. Original Gift; ex Hutton Castle, 1962. Inv. No. 142; Reg. No. 45.150.

45 Shield of NEVILLE of Hornby *(argent a saltire gules a label of three points argent);* pot metal; 11×9 in. 15th Century. Original Gift; ex Hutton Castle, 1962. Inv. No. 176; Reg. No. 45.156.

46 Shaped panel with angel holding the shield of TIERNEY *(argent a chevron sable a chief gules)* impaling WYDVILLE *(argent a fess and quarter gules)* quartering WOODHOUSE *(gules a cross or between twelve crosses crosslet fitchee argent)* and REDESWELL *(argent a chevron gules fretty or between three hinds' heads in profile gules)*; fragmentary architectural canopy with crocketted pinnacles in blue field; pot metal; abrasion; yellow stain; 40×16 in. 15th Century. Original Gift; ex Hutton Castle, 1956. Inv. No. 31; Reg. No. 45.134.

47 Shaped roundel with the shield of UPSALE *(argent a cross sable)* within a fragmentary border; pot metal; yellow stain (in border); dia. 15 in. 15th Century. Original Gift; ex Hutton Castle, 1962. Inv. No. 56; Reg. No. 45.138.

48 Shield of HUDDESFIELD *(argent on a fess between three boars passant sable a crescent argent)* impaling MATFORD, co. Devon *(argent a chevron gules between three quatrefoils slipped vert)*; pot metal; 8¾×7¼ in. 15th Century. Original Gift; ex Hutton Castle, 1956. Inv. No. 163; Reg. No. 153.

49 Shaped roundel with the shield of PHILPOT *(sable a bend ermine)* impaling CHIDEOK *(gules an escutcheon between eight martlets in orle argent)* within a fragmentary border; pot metal; yellow stain (in border); dia. 16 in. 15th Century. Original Gift; ex Hutton Castle, 1962. Inv. No. 54; Reg. No. 45.136.

50 Shaped roundel with the shield of HOLLAND *(per pale indented or and gules)* quartering LUCY ? *(azure three lions rampant argent)* and DREUX *(ermine)* and impaling CHIDEOK *(gules an escutcheon between eight martlets in orle argent)* within a fragmentary border; pot metal; yellow stain (in border); dia. 16 in. 15th Century. Original Gift; ex Hutton Castle, 1962. Inv. No. 55; Reg. No. 45.137.

51 Shield of ERPINGHAM *(vert an escutcheon between eight martlets in orle argent)* impaling CLOPTON *(sable a bend argent between two cotises dancetty or)*; pot metal; yellow stain (in border); 9¼×8¼ in. 15th Century. Original Gift; ex Hutton Castle, 1956. Inv. No. 164; Reg. No. 45.154.

52 Roundel with the shield of FITZALAN of Arundel *(gules a lion rampant or)* quartering MALTRAVERS *(sable fretty or)* within a fragmentary border; pot metal; yellow stain (in border); dia. 15 in. 15th Century. Original Gift; ex Hutton Castle, 1962. Inv. No. 57; Reg. No. 45.192.

53 Shaped panel with angel holding a shield bearing the ROYAL ARMS OF ENGLAND prior to 1340 differenced by a label of three points argent ; seemingly a companion panel to no. 46 but with a differently shaped architectural canopy; pot metal; yellow stain (in surround); 39¾ × 16 in. 15th Century. Original Gift; ex Hutton Castle, 1956. Inv. No. 28; Reg. No. 45.38a.

54 Shield with the ARMA CHRISTI *(the Sacred Heart and four wounds in a blue field):* pot metal; 12½ × 11 in. 15th Century. Ex Coll: A. L. Radford (said to be from the Becket window in Canterbury Cathedral). Original Gift; ex Hutton Castle, 1956. Inv. No. 29; Reg. No. 45.378.

55 Shield with the ARMA CHRISTI *(gules a cross crowned with thorns vert between in chief four nails and in base two scourges, over all a reed with sponge in bend dexter and a spear in bend sinister);* pot metal; 9¼ × 8 in. 15th Century. Original Gift; ex Hutton Castle, 1956. Inv. No. 93; Reg. No. 45.12.

56 Shield with the arms of BATTLE ABBEY *(argent a cross gules charged at fess point with a bishop's mitre argent and or, between in the first and fourth quarters a sword erect gules pommelled or and in the second and third quarters a crown or);* pot metal; yellow stain; 13 × 10½ in. 14th Century. Lit: Eden, The Connoisseur, Sept., 1930, p. 174 and January, 1931, p. 43; Newton, Scottish Art Review, Vol. VIII, No. 4, 1962. Original Gift (bought from Drake prior to 1930); ex Hutton Castle, 1956. Inv. No. 105; Reg. No. 45.120.

The Benedictine Abbey of St. Martin at Battle was founded by William the Conqueror and dedicated in 1095 by Anselm, Archbishop of Canterbury.

57 Shield of HENRY SPENCER, Bishop of Norwich (1370-1406) *(Despencer within a bordure charged with eight mitres or);* pot metal; yellow stain; 8 × 7 in. 15th Century. Original Gift; ex Hutton Castle, 1962. Inv. No. 143; Reg. No. 45.151.

The warlike Bishop of Norwich who suppressed Litester's rebels in 1381.

58 Roundel with the shaped shield of the GROCER'S COMPANY *(argent a chevron gules between nine cloves sable, three, three, and three)* within a floral border; pot metal; yellow stain; dia. 13 in. 16th Century. Original Gift; ex Hutton Castle. Inv. No. 309; Reg. No. 45.240.

The Worshipful Company of Grocers (anciently called the Pepperers) was incorporated 16th February, 1428, and received a grant of arms in 1531.

59 Unnamed shield of a bishop *(sable the hand of St. Thomas vested or touching the Sacred Heart gules between three spear heads or impaling argent a mitre ensigned with an archiepiscopal cross in bend sinister or)*; pot metal; yellow stain; $8 \times 7\frac{1}{2}$ in. 15th Century. Original Gift; ex Hutton Castle, 1962. Inv. No. 144; Reg. No. 45.152.

60 Panel with the shield of the Merchant Adventurers *(barry nebuly or and azure on a chief gules a lion of England quartering azure two roses or [sic for gules])*; pot metal abrasion; yellow stain; $17\frac{1}{2} \times 23$ in. Norwich School, 15th Century. Original Gift; ex Hutton Castle, 1956. Inv. No. 35; No. 45.40.

The Society of Merchant Adventurers (or Hambrough Merchants) was incorporated in 1296. The chief is quartered in reverse of the normal order.

61 Shield of CANTERBURY, PRIORY OF CHRIST CHURCH *(azure a cross argent charged with the letter X)* impaling GRYNDAL *(quarterly or and azure a cross quarterly ermines and or between four peahens collared counterchanged)*; pot metal; abrasion; yellow stain; $8\frac{1}{2} \times 7\frac{1}{2}$ in. 16th Century. Original Gift; ex Hutton Castle, 1956. Inv. No. 115; Reg. No. 45.208.

Edmund Gryndall, Archbishop of Canterbury, 1576-1583, received a grant of arms in 1559. See also no. 63.

62 Shield of PHILIPPE DE VILLIERS DE L'ISLE ADAM, Knight of Malta *(1)* and *(4)* de Villiers de l'Isle Adam; *(2)* and *(3)* de Chastillon; *over all on a chief gules a cross throughout argent for the Sovereign Military Order of Malta)*; pot metal; abrasion; yellow stain; $7\frac{1}{4} \times 6\frac{1}{2}$ in. 16th Century. Ex Coll: Lord Rochdale. Acquired per Surgey, 1948. Inv. No. 496, Reg. No. 45.291.

Later 13th Grand Master of the Sovereign Military Order of Malta (from 1530 until his death in 1534). See G. R. Gayre, The Heraldry of the Knights of St. John, 1958.

63 Shield of CANTERBURY, PRIORY OF CHRIST CHURCH, impaling EDMUND GRYNDAL, Archbishop of Canterbury, 1576-1583. Identical with No. 61. Original Gift; ex Hutton Castle, 1956. Inv. No. 116 ; Reg. No. 45.209.

64 Shield of CHERTSEY ABBEY *(per pale azure and or two keys in bend sinister and a sword in bend dexter points upward)*; pot metal; yellow stain; $8\frac{1}{4} \times 7\frac{1}{4}$ in. 15th Century. Original Gift; ex Hutton Castle. Inv. No. 299; Reg. No. 45.125.

The Benedictine Abbey at Chertsey, Surrey, was founded by Earconwald, Bishop of London, during the 8th century A.D.

65 Roundel with the shield of MAGDALEN COLLEGE, Oxford *(lozengy ermine and sable in a chief of the second three lilies argent)* within motto " Sanct Nomen eius fecit michi magna qui potens est "; pot metal; dia. $20\frac{1}{8}$ in. Late 15th Century. Original Gift; ex Hutton Castle, 1956. Inv. No. 102; Reg. No. 45.139.

The College of St. Mary Magdalen was founded by William Waynflete, Bishop of Winchester (licence granted 1457), whose arms became those of the College.

66 Shield of the ABBEY OF BURY ST. EDMUNDS *(azure three crowns or)*; pot metal; $9 \times 6\frac{3}{4}$ in. 15th Century. Original Gift; ex Hutton Castle, 1956. Inv. No. 103; Reg. No. 45.119.

The crown in base is not original.

67 Shield of the SEE OF WINCHESTER *(gules two keys addorsed or in bend sinister interlaced with a sword argent in bend dexter)*; pot metal; yellow stain; $11\frac{1}{2} \times 9\frac{1}{2}$ in. 15th Century. Original Gift; ex Hutton Castle, 1956. Inv. No. 119; Reg. No. 45.143.

68 Shield of TRINITY COLLEGE, Cambridge *(argent a chevron between three roses gules seeded or, in chief gules a lion of England between two closed books or)*; pot metal; abrasion; yellow stain; $9\frac{3}{4} \times 7\frac{1}{2}$ in. 16th Century. Ex Coll: Lord Rochdale. Lit: Eden, The Connoisseur, XCIV, 1934, p. 81, repro. VII. Acquired per Surgey, 1948. Inv. No. 521; Reg. No. 45.361.

The arms of Trinity College, founded in 1546, were confirmed at the Visitation of 1575.

69 Unnamed shield *(1) and (4) azure on a fess sable a portcullis between two fleurs de lys or; (2) and (3) gules an eagle displayed or; on an inescutcheon sable two keys in saltire and a crescent or );* pot metal; 9½ × 7¾ in. 16th Century. Acquired 1951. Inv. No. 564; Reg. No. 45.336.

70 Shield of BRENT, co. Kent *(gules on a wyvern's tail nowed argent a mullet sable);* pot metal; 9⅛ × 7⅞ in. 15th Century. Ex Coll: Dr. Philip Nelson. Original Gift; ex Hutton Castle. Inv. No. 408; Reg. No. 45.171.

71 Shield of JOHN COPLESTON, of Copleston, co. Devon *(argent a chevron engrailed gules between three leopards' faces azure langued gules);* pot metal; 8⅛ × 7¾ in. 15th Century. Ex Coll: A. L. Radford (in library of Bovey House). Lit: M. Drake, History of English Glass Painting, 1912, Pl. XII, fig. 6 (as from St. Edmund's-on-the-Bridge, Exeter, but possibly not identical). Original Gift; ex Hutton Castle, 1956. Inv. No. 123; Reg. No. 45.147.

Drake (op. cit.) notes remarkable use of double insertion, the tongues of the leopards being inserted into the faces which are themselves inserted into the field.

72 Shield of BRENT *(gules on a wyvern's tail nowed argent a mullet sable)* impaling BOSVILLE *(argent on a chevron azure three mullets or );* pot metal; 9⅛ × 7¾ in. 15th Century. Ex Coll: Dr. Philip Nelson. Original Gift; ex Hutton Castle. Inv. No. 409; Reg. No. 45.172. (See colour repro. p. 12).

73 Unnamed shield *(or a chevron ermine fimbriated gules between in chief two crosses flory and in base a horse's head erased sable);* pot metal; yellow stain; 8⅞ × 7⅛ in. 15th/16th Century. Acquired, 1951. Inv. No. 563; Reg. No. 45.335.

74 Shield of FITZALAN *(gules a lion rampant or)* quartering WARENNE *(chequy or and azure);* pot metal; yellow stain; 11¼ × 9¼ in. 14th Century. Original Gift; ex Hutton Castle. Inv. No. 306; Reg. No. 45.127.

Perhaps for Richard Fitzalan, 4th Earl of Arundel (beheaded 1397).

75 Unnamed shield *(or three bars and in chief a crescent gules)* impaling CHICHESTER *(chequy or and gules, a chief vair);* pot metal; 8½ × 7 in. 15th Century. Original Gift; ex Hutton Castle. Inv. No. 291; Reg. No. 45.165.

19

76  Shield of COPE *(argent on a chevron azure three lilies or all between three roses gules seeded or leafed and slipped vert)* impaling CRUWYS *(azure a bend per pale indented argent and gules all between six escallops or)*; pot metal; abrasion; yellow stain; 10×9½ in. 16th Century. Ex Coll: Lord Rochdale. Lit: Eden, The Connoisseur, XCIV, 1934, p. 81, repro. VI. Acquired per Surgey, 1948. Inv. No. 513; Reg. No. 45.292.

77  Shield of CRUWYS, of Cruwys Morchard, Co. Devon *(azure a bend per pale indented argent and gules all between six escallops or)*; pot metal; 9×7 in. Ex Coll: A. L. Radford *(*in library of Bovey House). 15th Century. Original Gift; ex Hutton Castle, 1956. Inv. No. 104; Reg. No. 45.140.

Said to be for Thomas Cruwys (living 1460) son of John Cruwys. The ruby glass in the bend is modern.

78  Shield of COPE impaling CRUWYS. Identical with No. 76. Original Gift; ex Hutton Castle. Inv. No. 304; Reg. No. 45.239.

79  Roundel with the shield of WINTERBOURNE *(argent a fess sable goutty of the first between three water-bougets of the second)* in fragmentary yellow stained surround; pot metal; dia. 12½ in. 16th Century. Original Gift; ex Hutton Castle, 1956. Inv. No. 194, Reg. No. 45.160.

80  Roundel with the shaped shield of LEWKNOR *(argent three chevrons azure)* impaled by LOVELACE *(gules on a chief indented sable three martlets argent)* quartering LOVELAS *(azure on a saltire engrailed argent five martlets sable)* within a wreath caught by gadrooned golden clasps; pot metal; yellow stain; dia. 13 in. Inscribed John Lewknor, 1548. Ex Coll: Hearst, New York. Original Gift; ex Hutton Castle. Inv. No. 301; Reg. No. 45.237. (See colour repro. p. 12).

81  Roundel with the shield of RADFORD *(quarterly of four)* impaling ST. ERMINE *(quartering Morton and Lovain)*; pot metal; abrasion; yellow stain; dia. 10¾ in. 16th Century. Ex Coll: Lord Rochdale. Lit: Eden, The Connoisseur, XCIV, 1934, p. 81. Acquired per Surgey, 1948. Inv. No. 518; Reg. No. 45.293.

The second and fourth dexter quarterings may be for Felbich and Aske.

82 Roundel with shield of WITHYPOULE *(per pale or and gules three lions passant guardant in pale within a bordure all counterchanged)* quartering PEMBRIGG and FORESTER within a fragmentary yellow stained border; pot metal; abrasion; yellow stain; dia. 14½ in. 16th Century. Original Gift; ex Hutton Castle, 1948. Inv. No. 222; Reg. No. 45.225.

83 Roundel with the shield of COMBERWORTH *(chequy or and gules on a chief argent a lion passant sable)* impaling KARDELEKE *(azure a tower embattled or);* pot metal; dia. 12¼ in. 15th Century. Ex Coll: Lord Rochdale. Lit: Eden, The Connoisseur, XCIV, 1934, p. 5, repro. IV. Acquired per Surgey, 1948. Inv. No. 515; Reg. No. 45.178.

84 Roundel with the shield of COMBERWORTH impaling ALLANSON *(azure three fleurs de lys or within a bordure gules);* pot metal; dia. 12¼ in. 15th Century. Ex Coll: Lord Rochdale. Lit: Eden, The Connoisseur, XCIV, 1934, p. 5, repro. V. Acquired per Surgey, 1948. Inv. No. 517; Reg. No. 45.179. (See colour repro. p. 12).

85 Roundel with the shield of JERNEGAN or JERNINGHAM *(argent three buckles lozengy gules)* impaling HARWARD *(azure on a fess paly of six gules and vert between three owls argent a mullet of the last);* pot metal; dia. 12 in. 15th Century. Ex Coll: Oswald Barron, F.S.A. Exhib: College of Arms, London (Herald's Commemorative Exhibition), 1934, No. 154. Acquired 1946; ex Hutton Castle, 1948. Inv. No. 422; Reg. No. 45.174. (See colour repro. p. 12).

An ancestor of the barons Stafford of Costessey Hall, some of whose collection of stained glass is in the Burrell Collection. (See nos. 6 and 9).

86 Roundel with the shield of BURNELL *(argent a lion rampant sable crowned or)* in fragmentary border; pot metal; yellow stain; dia. 15¾ in. 15th Century. Acquired per Drake, 1948. Inv. No. 482; Reg. No. 45.177.

87 Roundel with the shield of FRANCE *(azure three fleurs de lys or)* ensigned with a crown and two unicorn supporters; pot metal; yellow stain; dia. 15¼ in. 16th Century. Original Gift; ex Hutton Castle. Inv. No. 259; Reg. No. 45.227.

In a letter to Sir William Burrell dated 24th July, 1939, Wilfred Drake wrote: " I believe that your medallion belongs to the same series (as those in the Votive Kirk of St. Mary Magdalen, Cowgate, Edinburgh) and that all three may originally have been at Holyrood; painted for Mary Queen of Scots (and Queen of France) ".

88 Unnamed shield *(or a cross engrailed vert)* perhaps for DE NOON; pot metal; 6⅞×5⅜ in. 15th Century. Original Gift; ex Hutton Castle. Inv. No. 285; Reg. No. 45.230.

89 Garter medallion for FITZHUGH, K.G. *(azure, three chevrons braced, a chief or);* pot metal; yellow stain; 11½×8 in. 16th Century. Original Gift; ex Hutton Castle. Inv. No. 305; Reg. No. 45.167.

90 GEORGE NEVILLE (1497-1534), 5th Baron Abergavenny; circular garter medallion with shaped shield *(1) Neville of Raby; (2) Warenne; (3) Clare quartering Despencer; (4) Beauchamp);* pot metal; abrasion; yellow stain; 26½×15½ in. Inscribed: GEORGS NENVEL LORDE OF ABV . . . . . . . . ., 1558. 16th Century. Original Gift; ex Hutton Castle. Inv. No. 311; Reg. No. 45.241.

In 1558 the holder of the title was Henry Neville, 6th Lord Abergavenny (died 1586), son of the above.

91 Shield of CORBET *(1) or a raven sable; (2) Leybourne; (3) de Brus; (4) Lucy; (5) Trecarelle; (6) Burley; (7) Burley, Co. Salop);* pot metal; abrasion; yellow stain; 9×7¾ in. 16th Century. Original Gift; ex Hutton Castle, 1956. Inv. No. 124; Reg. No. 45.148.

92 Shield of LACY, co. Cornwall *(azure three swan's necks erased argent);* pot metal; 8⅞×7⅞ in. 15th Century. Acquired per Drake, 1945, ex Hutton Castle, 1948. Inv. No. 410; Reg. No. 45.363. (See colour repro. p. 12).

Perhaps for Edmund Lacy, Bishop of Exeter from 1420 until 1455.

93 Garter medallion with the shield of MOWBRAY *(gules a lion rampant argent)* quartering MALTRAVERS *(sable fretty or);* pot metal; abrasion; yellow stain; dia. 14¼ in. 16th Century. Original Gift; ex Hutton Castle, 1956. Inv. No. 178; Reg. No. 45.216.

94 Shield of ROSSETER, co. Lincoln *(argent on a bend gules three cinquefoils sable)* impaling MORTAINE *(ermine a chief indented gules);* pot metal; abrasion; 7½×6½ in. 15th Century. Original Gift; ex Hutton Castle. Inv. No. 308; Reg. No. 45.169.

95 Roundel with the shield of STANTER, of Horningsham, co. Wilts. *(sable a chevron ermine between three ducks argent all within a bordure engrailed of the second)* impaling SAWREY *(argent a bendlet azure between six lions rampant gules)*; pot metal; yellow stain (in border); dia. 12½ in. 16th Century. Acquired per Drake, 1946; ex Hutton Castle, 1948. Inv. No. 418; Reg. No. 45.246.

96 Unnamed shield *(sable a fleur de lys between three crescents argent within a bordure wavy ermine)*; pot metal; 7½×6 in. 16th Century. Original Gift; ex Hutton Castle. Inv. No. 283; Reg. No. 45.229.

97 Roundel with the shield of LISLE *(or on a chief azure three lions rampant of the first)*; pot metal; yellow stain (in border); dia. 13½ in. 15th Century. Original Gift; ex Hutton Castle, 1956. Inv. No. 30; Reg. No. 45.133. See No. 2 (Lisle impaling Stourton).

98 Roundel with the shield of STOURTON *(sable a bend or between six fountains)* within a red border; pot metal; dia. 8¼ in. 15th Century. Original Gift; ex Hutton Castle. Inv. No. 303; Reg. No. 45.166.

A classic example of canting arms, representing (according to Leland) the six springs of the river Stoure which rose three inside and three outside Stourton Park.

99 Panel with the arms of ARGENTE *(Gules three covered cups argent)*; pot metal; yellow stain; 18¼×13¼ in. 15th Century. Original Gift; ex Hutton Castle. 1956. Inv. No. 190; Reg. No. 45.159.

The Argente family, as lords of the manor of Great Wymondley, was entitled to the office of Chief Cupbearer at the Coronation.

100 Shield of HOPKINSON *(azure on a chevron between three estoiles or as many mascles sable in chief a cinquefoil)* impaling BURES *(ermine on a chief indented sable two lions rampant or)*; pot metal; yellow stain; 8¾×7¾ in. 16th Century. Original Gift; ex Hutton Castle. Inv. No. 343; Reg. No. 45.242.

101 Shield of a PRINCE OF WALES *(England and France quarterly with label of three points argent);* pot metal; $9\frac{3}{4} \times 7\frac{1}{2}$ in. 16th Century. Original Gift; ex Hutton Castle, 1956. Inv. No. 117; Reg. No. 45.141.

Richard II is said to have sometimes borne England quartering France (ancient) rather than the reverse, but France is here modern.

102 Panel with the ROYAL ARMS OF ENGLAND *(France and England quarterly)* within the garter ensigned by a crown and flanked by supporters (green otters but possibly bear cubs or boars rampant) in a surround of white quarries with yellow stain plant decoration; pot metal; yellow stain; $23\frac{3}{4} \times 17\frac{1}{2}$ in. 16th Century. Original Gift; ex Hutton Castle, 1948. Inv. No. 243, Reg. No. 45.161.

Possibly for Richard III (1452-85) who adopted two boars rampant argent tusked and bristled or as supporters.

103 Shield with the ROYAL ARMS OF ENGLAND *(France and England quarterly);* pot metal; $9\frac{1}{2} \times 8$ in. 16th Century. Original Gift; ex Hutton Castle, 1956. Inv. No. 118; Reg. No. 45.142.

104 Medallion with the ROYAL ARMS OF ENGLAND *(France and England quarterly)* ensigned with a crown and surrounded by a collar and the pendent badge of the Order of St. Michael; pot metal; yellow stain; $17 \times 11\frac{5}{8}$ in. 16th Century. Ex Coll: Hearst, New York. Original Gift; ex Hutton Castle. Inv. No. 294; Reg. No. 45.410. (See colour repro. p. 12).

The Order of St. Michael was instituted by Louise XI of France in 1469.

105 Medallion with the ROYAL ARMS OF ENGLAND *(France and England quarterly)* ensigned by a crown and surrounded by the garter and pendent cross pattee; pot metal; yellow stain; $22\frac{3}{4} \times 11\frac{3}{4}$ in. 16th Century. Ex Coll: Hearst, New York. Original Gift; ex Hutton Castle. Inv. No. 293; Reg. No. 45.233.

106 Shield with the ROYAL ARMS OF ENGLAND *(France and England quarterly);* pot metal; $11 \times 9$ in. 16th Century. Original Gift; ex Hutton Castle, 1956. Inv. No. 120; Reg. No. 45.144.

107 Shield *(tierced in pale; dexter: (1) Bavaria; (2) or a lion rampant sable; (3) Cleves; (4) argent a lion rampant gules crowned or; (5) argent a lion rampant azure crowned or; (6) or a fess chequy argent and gules; (7) argent three chevrons gules; (8) or a fess sable; an inescutcheon: sable a lion rampant within a bordure or; in pale: Pfalz am Rhein quartering Bavaria; an inescutcheon: argent a lion rampant azure crowned or; sinister: as dexter omitting first and fifth quarters);* silver stain, black, blue and red enamel; 7½×7 in. ? German, early 17th Century. Original Gift; ex Hutton Castle, Inv. No. 280; Reg. No. 45.350.

Described in inventory as the quarterings of Prince Rupert, son of Frederick V, Elector Palatine of the Rhine, by Elizabeth, daughter of James I of England.

108 Shield *(dexter: (1) and (4) or a lion rampant sable within a bordure or; (2) and (3) a lion rampant crowned or; an inescutcheon: argent, three chevrons gules; sinister: (1) and (4) an eagle displayed; (2) a griffin rampant; (3) or a lion rampant sable within a bordure compony argent and gules; an inescutcheon: quarterly argent and sable);* red pot metal; yellow stain; black enamel. 16¾×16¼ in. ? German, early 16th Century. Acquired per Drake, 1948. Inv. No. 486; Reg. No. 45.472.

Described in inventory as the Royal Arms of Flanders.

109 Unnamed lozenge shaped shield of a Lady *(sable a lion rampant or quartering azure an eagle crowned displayed or impaling gules five lozenges in cross argent between twenty billets or);* pot metal; abrasion; yellow stain; 9¾×8¾ in. Perhaps Dutch. 16th Century. Original Gift; ex Hutton Castle. Inv. No. 254; Reg. No. 45.99.

110 SIR FRANCIS KNOLLYS, K.G. (1514-1596) and his wife, CATHERINE CARY, niece of Anne Boleyn; shield *(Dexter: Knolles quartering Knowles; Sinister: Cary quarterly of twelve as in Nos. 176 and 243);* red pot metal; abrasion; yellow stain; blue enamel; 11×9¼ in. 16th Century. Original Gift; ex Hutton Castle, 1956. Inv. No. 111; Reg. No. 45.206.

Vice-Chamberlain 1559-1572; see also no. 112.

111 Panel with shield and mantling of NEVILLE, LORD ABERGAVENNY *(1)*
*Neville; (2) Neville of Bulmer; (3) Bulmer; (4) Boteler; (5) Beauchamp; (6) Abtot;*
*(7) Fitzalan; (8) Fitzalan; (9) Peverell; (10) Arundel; (11) Peverell; (12) Lupus;*
*(13) Plantagenet; (14) Warenne; (15) Clare; (16) Despencer; (17) Bradstone;*
*(18) Neville; at fess point a crescent or);* red pot metal; abrasion; yellow stain;
blue enamel; $10\frac{1}{8} \times 15$ in. Late 16th Century. Original Gift; ex Hutton
Castle. Inv. No. 302; Reg. No. 45.238.

112 ROBERT KNOLLYS (d. 1625) and his wife CATHERINE VAUGHAN, daughter
of Sir Roland Vaughan of Porthamel, Anglesey; shield *(Dexter: Knollys quartering
Knowles; Sinister: (1) Vaughan; (2) Segrave; (3) Baskerville; (4) Boteler; (5)
Unnamed; (6) Brayfield; (7) Egerton; (8) Morgan; (9) Boxall; (10) Cockaine;
(11) Powell; (12) Evans; (13) Goch of Gwent; (14) Bellewell; (15) Bate; (16)
Burnaville; (17) Fitz-Henry; (18) Lowe; (19) Parry; (20) Gunter; (21) Wolmer;
(22) Acton; (23) Hudleston; (24) Molyneux);* red pot metal; abrasion; yellow
stain; blue enamel; $10\frac{3}{4} \times 9\frac{1}{4}$ in. 16th Century. Original Gift; ex Hutton Castle,
1956. Inv. No. 112; Reg. No. 45.207.

Fourth son of Francis Knollys; Usher of the Mint in the Tower of London, 1578.
According to the inventory nos. 110 and 112 were probably painted for the Knollys'
seat at Rotherfield Grays in Oxfordshire, c. 1575.

113 Roundel with shield of JOHN BOURCHIER, EARL OF BATH (d. 1556) *(1)*
*Bourchier and Lovain debruised by a label of three points azure each charged with as many
fleurs de lys or; (2) Fitzwarin; (3) Audley; (4) Cogan; (5) Hanckford; (6) Hankford;
(7) Martyn; (8) Neville; (9) Arches)* in yellow stain grotesque border; pot metal;
abrasion; yellow stain; enamel; dia. $14\frac{1}{4}$ in. 16th Century. Original Gift; ex
Hutton Castle. Inv. No. 292; Reg. No. 45.232.

114 Garter medallion with the shield of ROBERT DUDLEY (? 1532-1588), K.G.
EARL OF LEICESTER *(1) Dudley; (2) Somery; (3) Grey; (4) Hastings;
(5) Valence; (6) Ferrers; (7) Quincy; (8) Beaumont; (9) Talbot; (10) Beauchamp;
(11) Newburgh; (12) Berkeley; (13) Lisle; (14) Guilford; (15) West; (16) Mortimer);* red pot metal; abrasion; yellow stain; blue enamel; dia. $16\frac{3}{4}$ in. Late
16th Century. Original Gift; ex Hutton Castle, 1956. Inv. No. 101; Reg. No.
45.205.

Third son of John Dudley, Duke of Northumberland, and Jane Guildford; brother
of Lady Jane Grey; favourite of Queen Elizabeth.

115 JOHN DE VERE (1442-1484), 13th Earl of Oxford, P.C., K.G., garter medallion with shaped shield *(Dexter: (1) and (4) De Vere; (2) and (3) Howard; Sinister: (1) and (4) Montagu quartering Monthermer; (2) and (3) Neville);* pot metal; abrasion; yellow stain; dia. 16¼ in. 16th Century. Ex Coll: Fawsley Hall. Acquired per Grosvenor Thomas, 1950. Inv. No. 553; Reg. No. 45.325.

Second, but first surviving, son of John de Vere, 12th Earl, and Elizabeth Howard; married Margaret, daughter of Richard Neville, Earl of Salisbury by Alice, daughter of Thomas Montagu, 4th Earl of Salisbury; Hereditary Lord Great Chamberlain of England.

116 ROBERT DE VERE (b. 1257), 6th Earl of Oxford; roundel with fragmentary border enclosing shaped shield *(De Vere impaling Mortimer);* pot metal; dia. 16 in. 16th Century. Ex Coll: Fawsley Hall. Acquired per Grosvenor Thomas, 1950. Inv. No. 554; Reg. No. 45.326.

Robert, 6th Earl, married Margaret, sister of Edmund, 1st Lord Mortimer, of Wigmore, and daughter of Roger de Mortimer.

117 HUGH DE VERE (c. 1210-c. 1263), 4th Earl of Oxford; wreath border enclosing shaped shield *(De Vere impaling De Quincy);* pot metal; abrasion; yellow stain; dia. 17¾ in. 16th Century. Ex Coll: Fawsley Hall. Acquired per Grosvenor Thomas, 1950. Inv. No. 558; Reg. No. 45.330.

Hugh, 4th Earl, married Hawise, daughter of Saher de Quincy, 1st Earl of Winchester; officiated as Master Chamberlain of England at the coronation of Queen Eleanor in 1236.

118 RICHARD DE VERE (b. c. 1385), 11th Earl of Oxford, K.G.; garter medallion with shaped shield *(De Vere impaling Sergeaux quartering Arundel);* pot metal; abrasion; yellow stain; dia. 16 in. 16th Century. Ex Coll: Fawsley Hall. Acquired per Grosvenor Thomas, 1950. Inv. No. 556; Reg. No. 45.328.

Richard, 11th Earl, married Alice, sister and co-heir of Richard Sergeaux, and third daughter of Sir Richard Sergeaux by Philippe, daughter and co-heir of Sir Edmund de Arundel; fought at Agincourt; K.G. May, 1416.

Cat. No. 122

119 Roundel with the shaped shield of DE VERE impaling HUME *(vert a lion rampant argent langued or);* pot metal; abrasion; yellow stain; dia. 17¼ in. 16th Century. Ex Coll: Fawsley Hall. Acquired per Grosvenor Thomas, 1950. Inv. No. 559; Reg. No. 45.331. (See colour repro. p. 29).

120 Roundel with the shaped shield of DE VERE impaling CLARE *(or three chevrons gules);* pot metal; abrasion; yellow stain; dia. 17 in. 16th Century. Ex Coll: Fawsley Hall. Acquired per Grosvenor Thomas, 1950. Inv. No. 557; Reg. No. 45.329.

121 Roundel with the shaped shield of DE VERE impaling MARSHAL, Earl of Pembroke *(per pale or and vert a lion rampant gules);* pot metal; abrasion; yellow stain; dia. 18¼ in. 16th Century. Ex Coll: Fawsley Hall. Acquired per Grosvenor Thomas, 1950. Inv. No. 555; Reg. No. 45.327.

122 Panel with the helm, mantling *(ermine)*, crest *(a buck's head couped argent attired or)*, supporters *(golden falcon for Skenard and blue boar for De Vere)* and shaped shield of SIR EDMUND KNIGHTLEY OF FAWSLEY (d. 1542) and his wife URSULA VERE *(Dexter: (1) and (17) Knightley; (2) and (18) Duston; (3) and (13) Skenard; (4) and (14) Harowdon; (5) and (15) St. John; (6) and (16) Bagot; (7) and (23) Burgh; (8) and (24) Cowley; (9) and (19) Combemartin; (10) and (20) Lion; (11) and (21) Dillon Lee, (12) and (22) Thorleys; Sinister: De Vere quartering Howard);* pot metal; abrasion; yellow stain; 30¾ × 18½ in. 16th Century. Ex Coll: Fawsley Hall. Acquired per Grosvenor Thomas, 1950. Inv. No. 560; Reg. No. 45.332.

" Sir Edmund Knightley . . . . added a splendid shield to the Knightley matches for his wife was a sister and co-heir of John Vere, the 14th Earl of Oxford. He is said to have finished the work upon the great Hall at Fawsley where his arms are in the window supported by the blue boar of Vere and the golden falcon of the Skenards . . . . He left no one of his six daughters surviving at his death and Fawsley was in turn enjoyed by Sir Valentine Knightley " (Northamptonshire Families, ed. Barron, 1906, p. 171). For the arms of Sir Valentine, brother of Sir Edmund, see no. 148.

# Fawsley Hall

Cat. No. 119

Cat. No. 132

Cat. No. 150

Cat. No. 153

123 JOHN KNIGHTLEY OF GNOSALL, Staffordshire, and his wife ELISABETH BURGH; panel with hour-glass shaped shield *(Dexter: (1) and (4) Knightley; (2) and (3) Duston; Sinister: (1) and (4) Burgh; (2) and (3) Cowley)*; pot metal; abrasion; yellow stain; 19½ × 16½ in. 16th Century. Ex Coll: Fawsley Hall. Acquired per Grosvenor Thomas, 1950. Inv. No. 523; Reg. No. 45.295.

John Knightley of Gnosall (d. 1413), 8th in the line of descent, married Elisabeth, daughter of Adam Burgh, and grand-daughter and heir of William of Burgh, Lord of Burgh Hall in Gnosall, which William had married Eleanor, daughter and heir of John Cowley of Cowley. By this marriage Burgh Hall came to the Knightleys.

124 Panel with hour-glass shaped shield of KNIGHTLEY *(quarterly ermine and paly of six gules and or)* quartering DUSTON *(azure a buck's head cabossed or)* and BURGH *(argent on a saltire sable five ducks of the field)*; pot metal; abrasion; yellow stain; 19½ × 17 in. 16th Century. Ex Coll: Fawsley Hall. Acquired per Grosvenor Thomas, 1950. Inv. No. 524; Reg. No. 45.296. The 4th quarter is a replacement.

125 RICHARD KNIGHTLEY OF GNOSALL and his wife JOAN GIFFARD; panel with hour-glass shaped shield *(Knightley impaling Giffard)*; pot metal;

abrasion; yellow stain; 19½ × 16½ in. 16th Century. Ex Coll: Fawsley Hall. Acquired per Grosvenor Thomas, 1950. Inv. No. 526; Reg. No. 45.298.

Joan Giffard, wife of Richard Knightley of Gnosall, 9th in line of descent, was probably daughter of John Giffard of Chillington in Staffordshire.

126 Panel with hour-glass shaped shield of GIFFARD *(azure three stirrups or with their leathers)*; impaling COWLEY *(gules a chevron compony or and argent between three crosses flory of the last)*; pot metal; abrasion; yellow stain; 19¾ × 16¾ in. 16th Century. Ex Coll: Fawsley Hall. Acquired per Grosvenor Thomas, 1950. Inv. No. 533; Reg. No. 45.305.

127 RICHARD KNIGHTLEY OF FAWSLEY and his wife ELIZABETH PUREFOY; panel with hour-glass shaped shield *(Dexter: (1) Knightley; (2) Duston; (3) Burgh; (4) Cowley; Sinister: (1) and (4) Purefoy, co. Bucks.; (2) and (3) Purefoy, co. Leicester)*; pot metal; abrasion; yellow stain; 19½ × 16½ in. 16th Century. Ex Coll: Fawsley Hall. Acquired per Grosvenor Thomas, 1950. Inv. No. 522; Reg. No. 45.294.

Richard Knightley (d. 1443), 10th in line of descent, was the first Knightley of Fawsley, co. Northampton, which manor he acquired in 1416. His wife was the daughter of Thomas Purefoy of Drayton.

128 Panel with hour-glass shaped shield of PUREFOY, co. Bucks. *(gules three pairs of hands couped hand in hand)* quartering PUREFOY, co. Leicester *(azure three stirrups or)* impaling DUSTON *(azure a buck's head cabossed or)* quartering FOULESHURST *(gules fretty or a chief argent )* and CATESBY *(argent two lions passant sable crowned or)*; pot metal; abrasion; yellow stain; 19½ × 17 in. 16th Century. Ex Coll: Fawsley Hall. Acquired per Grosvenor Thomas, 1950. Inv. No. 532; Reg. No. 45.304

Richard Knightley held the manor of Fawsley jointly with his wife Elizabeth and Robert Catesby.

129 Panel with the hour-glass shaped shield of DILLON-LEE *(argent a fess azure between three crescents gules)* impaling THORLEYS *(gules on a chief argent five lozenges gules fesswise)*; pot metal; yellow stain; 19½ × 16½ in. 16th Century. Ex Coll: Fawsley Hall. Acquired per Grosvenor Thomas, 1950. Inv. No. 527; Reg. No. 45.299.

This and the following thirteen panels (nos. 129 to 142) represent the maternal ancestors of Jane Skenard, wife of Sir Richard Knightley of Fawsley (d. 1534). Her mother, Marjery, was sister and heir of Thomas Harwedon (or Harowdon).

130 Panel with the hour-glass shaped shield of DILLON-LEE quartering THORLEYS; pot metal; yellow stain; 19 × 16 in. 16th Century. Ex Coll: Fawsley Hall. Acquired per Grosvenor Thomas, 1950. Inv. No. 528; Reg. No. 45.300.

131 Panel with the hour-glass shaped shield of ST. JOHN *(gules two bars argent, a canton ermine)* impaling BAGOT *(argent a chevron gules between three martlets sable)*; pot metal; yellow stain; 19 × 16½ in. 16th Century. Ex Coll: Fawsley Hall. Acquired per Grosvenor Thomas, 1950. Inv. No. 529; Reg. No. 45.301.

132 Panel with the hour-glass shaped shield of ST. JOHN *(gules two bars argent a canton ermine)* quartering BAGOT *(argent a chevron gules between three martlets sable)*; pot metal; yellow stain; 19 × 16 in. 16th Century. Ex Coll: Fawsley Hall. Acquired per Grosvenor Thomas, 1950. Inv. No. 531; Reg. No. 45.303. (See colour repro. p. 29).

133 Panel with the hour-glass shaped shield of ST. JOHN *(gules two bars argent a canton ermine)* quartering BAGOT *(argent a chevron gules between three martlets sable)* impaling COMBEMARTIN *(gules a lion rampant vair);* pot metal ; yellow stain ; $19\frac{1}{4} \times 16\frac{1}{4}$ in. 16th Century. Ex Coll: Fawsley Hall. Acquired per Grosvenor Thomas, 1950. Inv. No. 530; Reg. No. 45.302.

134 Panel with the hour-glass shaped shield of ST. JOHN *(gules two bars argent a canton ermine)* quartering BAGOT *(argent a chevron gules between three martlets sable)* and COMBEMARTIN *(gules a lion rampant vair);* pot metal; yellow stain; $19\frac{1}{2} \times 16\frac{1}{2}$ in. 16th Century. Ex Coll: Fawsley Hall. Acquired per Grosvenor Thomas, 1950. Inv. No. 525; Reg. No. 45.297.

135 Panel with the hour-glass shaped shield of HAROWDON *(argent on a bend gules five lozenges or)* impaling ST. JOHN, BAGOT, COMBEMARTIN, LION, DILLON-LEE and THORLEYS; pot metal; abrasion; yellow stain; $18 \times 15\frac{3}{4}$ in. 16th Century. Ex Coll: Fawsley Hall. Acquired per Grosvenor Thomas, 1950. Inv. No. 537; Reg. No. 45.309.

136 Panel with the hour-glass shaped shield of HAROWDON quartering ST. JOHN, BAGOT, COMBEMARTIN, LION, DILLON-LEE and THORLEYS; pot metal; abrasion; yellow stain ; $17\frac{3}{4} \times 16$ in. 16th Century. Ex Coll: Fawsley Hall. Acquired per Grosvener Thomas, 1950. Inv. No. 538; Reg. No. 45.310.

137 Panel with the hour-glass shaped shield of HAROWDON quartering ST. JOHN, BAGOT, COMBEMARTIN, LION, DILLON-LEE and THORLEYS impaling VAUX *(chequy argent and gules on a chevron azure three cinquefoils or)* quartering SHARPE *(argent three rooks' heads erased sable);* pot metal; abrasion; yellow stain. $17\frac{3}{4} \times 15\frac{1}{2}$ in. 16th Century. Ex Coll: Fawsley Hall. Acquired per Grosvenor Thomas, 1950. Inv. No. 541; Reg. No. 45.313.

138 Panel with the hour-glass shaped shield of ST. JOHN, BAGOT, COMBEMARTIN quartering LION, DILLON-LEE, THORLEYS; pot metal; abrasion; yellow stain; 17 × 14¾ in. 16th Century. Ex Coll: Fawsley Hall. Acquired per Grosvenor Thomas, 1950. Inv. No. 543; Reg. No. 45.315.

139 Panel with the hour-glass shaped shield of LION *(argent a lion rampant gules)* impaling DILLON-LEE *(argent a fess azure between three crescents gules)* quartering THORLEYS *(gules on a chief argent five lozenges gules fesswise);* pot metal; yellow stain; 18 × 15½ in. 16th Century. Ex Coll: Fawsley Hall. Acquired per Grosvenor Thomas, 1950. Inv. No. 542; Reg. No. 45.314.

140 Panel with the hour-glass shaped shield of LION quartering DILLON-LEE and THORLEYS; pot metal; abrasion; yellow stain; 17¼ × 16 in. 16th Century. Ex Coll: Fawsley Hall. Acquired per Grosvenor Thomas, 1950. Inv. No. 539; Reg. No. 45.311.

141 Panel with the hour-glass shaped shield of SKENARD *(sable a chevron between three hawks' lures argent)* impaling HAROWDON, ST. JOHN, BAGOT, COMBE-MARTIN, LION, DILLON-LEE, THORLEYS; pot metal; abrasion; yellow stain; 17¾ × 15¼ in. 16th Century. Ex Coll: Fawsley Hall. Acquired per Grosvenor Thomas, 1950. Inv. No. 545; Reg. No. 45.317.

This shield is for Henry Skenard and his wife Margery, sister and heir of Thomas Harwedon (or Harowdon). Their daughter Jane married Sir Richard Knightley (d. 1534), 12th in the line of descent, and the shields of their sons, daughter, and grandson are shown in nos. 122, 148, 149 and 150. Jane Skenard, wife of Sir Richard, died about 1539 and was buried with her husband in Fawsley Church where their tomb remains.

142 Panel with the hour-glass shaped shield of SKENARD quartering HAROWDON, ST. JOHN, BAGOT, COMBEMARTIN, LION, DILLON-LEE, THORLEYS; pot metal; abrasion; yellow stain; 18 × 15¾ in. 16th Century. Ex Coll: Fawsley Hall. Acquired per Grosvenor Thomas, 1950. Inv. No. 540; Reg. No. 45.312.

The shield for Sir Richard Knightley and his wife Jane Skenard, i.e. Knightley impaling Skenard, is missing from the series.

143 Panel with the hour-glass shaped shield of KING EDWARD THE CONFESSOR *(azure a cross patonce between five martlets or in orle)*; pot metal; yellow stain; 18 × 16 in. 16th Century. Ex Coll: Fawsley Hall. Acquired per Grosvenor Thomas, 1950. Inv. No. 534; Reg. No. 45.306.

Arms attributed to various early kings and adopted by Richard II and University College, Oxford.

144 Panel with the hour-glass shaped shield with the ROYAL ARMS OF ENGLAND *(France and England quarterly)*; pot metal; abrasion; yellow stain; 18 × 16 in. 16th Century. Ex Coll: Fawsley Hall. Acquired per Grosvenor Thomas, 1950. Inv. No. 535; Reg. No. 45.307.

The side segments bear the red roses of Lancaster (with abraded yellow centres).

145 Panel with the hour-glass shaped shield of CASTILE *(gules a castle or)* and LEON *(argent a lion rampant gules)* quartering ARAGON *(paly of eight or and gules)* and SICILY *(per saltire argent two eagles displayed sable and paly of eight gules and or)*; pot metal; abrasion; yellow stain; 17¾ × 15¾ in. 16th Century. Ex Coll: Fawsley Hall. Acquired per Grosvenor Thomas, 1950. Inv. No. 536; Reg. No. 45.308.

The side segments bear the split pomegranates of Aragon. These two shields, Nos. 144 and 145, were doubtless for Henry VIII and his first wife Catherine of Aragon (marriage annulled in 1533).

146 Panel with the hour-glass shaped shield of ST. GEORGE *(argent a cross gules)*; pot metal; $17\frac{3}{4} \times 15\frac{1}{2}$ in. 16th Century. Ex Coll: Fawsley Hall. Acquired per Grosvenor Thomas, 1950. Inv. No. 544; Reg. No. 45.316.

This shield in combination with the royal arms may be for Henry VIII as Sovereign of the Order of the Garter.

147 Shaped medallion with the arms of Henry VIII AND JANE SEYMOUR *(France and England quarterly impaling (1) Seymour augmentation; (2) Seymour; (3) Beauchamp; (4) Esturmy; (5) MacWilliam; (6) Coker)*; shield set in a richly ornamented wreath above the words: DIEU ET MON DROYT, 1580; pot metal; abrasion; yellow stain; $24 \times 16\frac{1}{2}$ in. 16th Century. Ex Coll: Fawsley Hall. Acquired per Grosvenor Thomas, 1950. Inv. No. 546; Reg. No. 318.

148 Shaped medallion with shield of SIR VALENTINE KNIGHTLEY (d. 1566) and his wife ANNE FERRERS *(Dexter: (1) Knightley; (2) Duston; (3) Burgh; (4) Cowley; (5) Skenard; (6) Harowdon; (7) St. John; (8) Bagot; (9) Lion; (10) Combemartin; (11) Dillon-Lee; (12) Thorleys. Sinister: (1) Ferrers of Groby; (2) Ferrers; (3) Botetourt; (4) or a cross gules; (5) Mountford; at fess point a crescent argent)*; shield set in a richly ornamented wreath above the words: Sir Valentine Knightley Fares, 1572; pot metal; abrasion; yellow stain; $24 \times 18\frac{1}{2}$ in. 16th Century. Ex Coll: Fawsley Hall. Acquired per Grosvenor Thomas, 1950. Inv. No. 547; Reg. No. 45.319.

Sir Valentine was the third son of Sir Richard Knightley by Joan Skenard to own Fawsley Hall, and he became the ancestor of all succeding Knightleys, the six daughters of his elder brother Sir Edmund having died young. He married Anne Ferrers, daughter of Sir Edward Ferrers of Baddesley Clinton in Warwickshire. She died in 1554.

149  Shaped medallion with shield of SIR WILLIAM SPENCER (d. 1532) of Althorp, and his wife SUSAN KNIGHTLEY *(Dexter: azure a fess ermine between three seamews' heads erased argent for Spencer. Sinister: Knightley quarterly of twelve as in nos. 148 and 150);* shield set in richly ornamented wreath above the words: Sir William Spencer Knightley 1572; pot metal; abrasion; yellow stain; $23\frac{3}{4} \times 17\frac{1}{2}$ in. 16th Century. Ex Coll: Fawsley Hall.  Acquired per Grosvenor Thomas, 1950.  Inv. No. 548; Reg. No. 45.320.

Susan Knightley, sister of Sir Valentine, married Sir William Spencer of Althorp, from whom descended the Dukes of Marlborough and the Earls Spencer.  Her eldest brother, Richard Knightley of Upton (d. 1537) married her husband's sister, Jane Spencer.

150  Shaped medallion with the shield of SIR RICHARD KNIGHTLEY (d. 1615) and his wife MARY FERMOR *(Dexter: Knightley quarterly of twelve as in nos. 148 and 149; Sinister: argent on a fess sable three anchors or between three lions' heads erased gules);* shield set in richly ornamented wreath above a blank cartouche; pot metal; abrasion; yellow stain; $23\frac{1}{2} \times 18\frac{1}{4}$ in. 16th Century.  Ex Coll: Fawsley Hall. Acquired per Grosvenor Thomas, 1950.  Inv. No. 549; Reg. No. 45.321. (See colour repro. p. 29).

Sir Richard, eldest son of Sir Valentine Knightley, died in 1615 at the age of eighty-two.  His first wife, Mary Fermor died in 1573 and he married secondly Elizabeth Seymour, daughter of the Duke of Somerset.

151  Garter medallion ensigned by an earl's coronet with the shield of AMBROSE DUDLEY, Earl of Warwick, K.G. *(1) Somery; (2) Beaumont; (3) Grey; (4) Belesme, for Talbot; (5) Beauchamp; (6) Newburgh, for Warwick; (7) Guildford; (8) Mortimer; at fess point a besant);* the garter enriched with scroll-work; pot metal; abrasion; yellow stain; $26\frac{1}{2} \times 17$ in. 16th Century. Ex. Coll: Fawsley Hall.  Acquired per Grosvenor Thomas, 1950.  Inv. No. 552; Reg. No. 45.324.

152 Garter medallion ensigned by a coronet with the shield of WILLIAM PARR, EARL OF ESSEX, K.G. *(1) Parr; (2) Parr; (3) Fitzhugh; (4) Garnegan; (5) Furneaulx; (6) Grey; (7) Marmion; (8) Garnegan; (9) St. Quintin; (10) Green; (11) Mablethorpe);* the garter enriched with scroll-work; pot metal; abrasion; yellow stain; $26\frac{3}{4} \times 17\frac{1}{2}$ in. 16th Century. Ex Coll: Fawsley Hall. Acquired per Grosvenor Thomas, 1950. Inv. No. 551; Reg. No. 45.323.

William Parr (1513-1571), brother of Katherine Parr, sixth and last queen consort of Henry VIII, was the son and heir of Sir Thomas Parr, of Kendal, Westmorland, and of Parr in Prescot, Lancashire, by Maud, daughter and co-heir of Sir Thomas Green, of Green's Norton, Northants. He was made Earl of Essex and Knight of the Garter in 1543; Marquess of Northampton 1546/7; attainted 1553 with loss of earldom and other honours; restored as marquess 1558/9.

153 Garter medallion ensigned by a cap of maintenance and crown surmounted by cross and orb with the ROYAL ARMS OF ENGLAND *(France and England quarterly);* pot metal; abrasion; yellow stain; $26\frac{1}{4} \times 14\frac{1}{4}$ in. 16th Century. Ex Coll: Fawsley Hall. Acquired per Grosvenor Thomas, 1950. Inv. No. 550; Reg. No. 45.322. (See colour repro. p. 29).

The lilies are inserted; the lions abraded; the second quarter is a recent restoration.

154 Circular garter medallion with the ROYAL ARMS OF ENGLAND *(France and England quarterly);* pot metal; abrasion; yellow stain; $16\frac{1}{2} \times 13\frac{1}{4}$ in. 16th Century. Ex Coll: Vale Royal (Saloon, east window). Lit: The Genealogist, XXXVIII, 1921-2, 81. Acquired per Drake, 1947. Inv. No. 443; Reg. No. 45.252. (See colour repro. p. 44).

155 Oval medallion with the ROYAL ARMS OF ENGLAND *(France and England quarterly);* shaped shield set in diapered pink surround of later date; pot metal; $14\frac{1}{4} \times 11\frac{3}{4}$ in. 16th Century. Ex Coll: Vale Royal (Saloon, west window). Lit: The Genealogist, XXXVIII, 1921-2, 59. Acquired per Drake, 1947. Inv. No. 444; Reg. No. 45.253.

156 Oval medallion ensigned by a red rose with the arms of HENRY VIII AND JANE SEYMOUR *(France and England impaling (1) Seymour augmentation; (2) Seymour; (3) Beauchamp of Hache; (4) Esturmi; (5) MacWilliam; (6) Coker);* pot metal; abrasion; yellow stain; ∤16⅛×11⅛ in. 16th Century. Ex Coll: Vale Royal (Saloon, east window). Lit: The Genealogist, XXXVIII, 1921-2, 73. Acquired per Drake, 1947. Inv. No. 446; Reg. No. 45.255.

See also nos. 298 and 300.

157 Circular medallion ensigned by a crown with the arms of HENRY VIII AND JANE SEYMOUR *(France and England quarterly impaling (1) Seymour; (2) Seymour augmentation; (3) Beauchamp of Hache; (4) Esturmi; ¦ (5) MacWilliam; (6) Coker);* shaped shield set in a chaplet of red and white roses ; pot metal ; abrasion; yellow stain; 17½×11¼ in. 16th Century. Ex Coll: Vale Royal (Saloon, west window). Lit: The Genealogist, XXXVIII, 1921-2, 64(?). Acquired per Drake, 1947. Inv. No. 447, Reg. No. 45.256.

158 Circular garter medallion ensigned by a crown with the arms of EDWARD, PRINCE OF WALES (afterwards Edward VI); shaped shield *(France and England quarterly with a label of three points argent)*; pot metal; abrasion; yellow stain; 17¼× 12¼ in. 16th Century. Ex Coll: Vale Royal (Saloon, east window). Lit: The Genealogist, XXXVIII, 1921-2, 75. Acquired per Drake, 1947. Inv. No. 448; Reg. No. 45.257.

159 Circular garter medallion ensigned by a crown with arms perhaps for PRINCE EDWARD OF WINDSOR (afterwards Edward III); shaped shield *(France ancient quartering England with label of three points argent);* pot metal; abrasion; yellow stain; 17×12 in. 16th Century. Ex Coll: Vale Royal (Entrance Hall, east window). Lit: The Genealogist, XXXVIII, 1921-2, 49. Acquired per Drake, 1947. Inv. No. 449; Reg. No. 45.258.

160 Circular garter medallion ensigned by a coronet with the shaped shield of EDWARD
STANLEY, 3rd EARL OF DERBY, K.G. *(1) Stanley; (2) Lathom; (3) Man;
(4) Warenne; (5) Strange; (5) Woodville; (6) Mohun; (8) Montalt);* pot metal;
abrasion; yellow stain; 18½ × 13¼ in. 16th Century. Ex Coll: Vale Royal (Saloon,
west window). Lit: The Genealogist, XXXVIII, 1921-2, 68. Acquired per
Drake, 1947. Inv. No. 451; Reg. No. 45.260.

The 3rd Earl (d. 1572) was created K.G. in 1547; for a discussion of his arms
see F. A. Bailey, " Some Stanley Heraldic Glass from Warden Hall, Lancs." in
T. of Hist. Soc. Lancs. and Ches., Vol. 101, 1950, pp. 69-84.

161 Circular garter medallion with the straight-sided shield of HENRY FITZALAN,
12th EARL OF ARUNDEL, K.G. *(1) Fitzalan; (2) Fitzalan of Bedale impaling
Montboucher; (3) Woodville; (4) Maltravers quartering Fitzalan of Clun);* pot metal;
abrasion; yellow stain; dia. 14½ in. 16th Century. Ex Coll: Vale Royal (Saloon,
east window). Lit: The Genealogist, XXXVIII, 1921-2, 79. Acquired per
Drake, 1947. Inv. No. 452; Reg. No. 45.261.

Born in 1512; created K.G. 1544; acted as High Constable at the coronation
of Edward VI; served on the commission for the trial of Mary, Queen of Scots
in 1568; died in 1580.

162 Circular garter medallion ensigned by a coronet with the shaped shield of FRANCIS
TALBOT, 5th EARL OF SHREWSBURY *(1) Belesme; (2) Talbot; (3) Valetort;
(4) Valence; (5) Neville; (6) Furnival; (7) Verdon; (8) Strange; (9) Lovetot);*
pot metal; abrasion; yellow stain; 17 × 13½ in. 16th Century. Ex Coll: Vale
Royal (Entrance Hall, east window). Lit: The Genealogist, XXXVIII, 1921-2,
47. Acquired per Drake, 1947. Inv. No. 453; Reg. No. 45.262.

Born 1500; succeeded 1538; created K.G. 1545; appointed chief commissioner
to hear claims at the coronation of Queen Elizabeth in 1558.

163 Circular garter medallion with shaped shield of FRANCIS TALBOT, 5th EARL
OF SHREWSBURY, K.G.; similar to no. 162 but with smaller coronet and
the 7th quarter *(Verdun)* preserved; pot metal; abrasion; yellow stain; $16\frac{1}{2} \times$
$13\frac{1}{2}$ in. 16th Century. Ex Coll: Vale Royal (Saloon, west window). Lit: The
Genealogist, XXXVIII, 1921-2, 69. Acquired per Drake, 1947. Inv. No. 454;
Reg. No. 45.263.

164 Circular garter medallion ensigned by an earl's coronet with the shaped shield of
EDWARD STANLEY, 3rd EARL OF DERBY, K.G.; similar to no. 160 but
with leaf motive instead of scroll on either side of shield ; pot metal; abrasion;
yellow stain; $18\frac{3}{4} \times 13\frac{1}{2}$ in. 16th Century. Ex Coll: Vale Royal (Saloon, west
window). Lit: The Genealogist, XXXVIII, 1921-2, 72. Acquired per Drake,
1947. Inv. No. 456; Reg. No. 45.265.

165 Circular garter medallion ensigned by a fragmentary royal crown with straight-
sided shield *(1)* and *(4)* Neville of Raby (rose on saltire missing); *(2)* Woodstock
*(lions argent for or); (3) Neville of Bulmer);* pot metal; abrasion; yellow stain;
$18 \times 14\frac{1}{2}$ in. 16th Century. Ex Coll: Vale Royal (Saloon, west window). Lit:
The Genealogist, XXXVIII, 1921-2, 65. Acquired per Drake 1947. Inv. No. 455;
Reg. No. 45.264.

Called George Neville, Lord Bergavenny, created K.G. in 1513, died 1535, in
Genealogist (op. cit.) and Richard Neville, Earl of Warwick, in inventory.

166 Circular garter medallion ensigned by an earl's coronet with the shaped shield of
SIR WILLIAM PAULET, 1st EARL OF WILTSHIRE, K.G. *(1)* Paulet; *(2)*
*Roos of Gedney; (3) Poynings; (4) St. John; (5) Delamere; (6) Hussey; (7) Skelton;*
*(8) Irby; (9) Delamore);* on either side of shield a scroll inscribed: Erle of Wylshire;
pot metal; abrasion; yellow stain; $17\frac{1}{2} \times 13\frac{1}{2}$ in. 16th Century. Ex Coll: Vale
Royal (Saloon, west window). Lit: The Genealogist, XXXVIII, 1921-2, 67.
Acquired per Drake, 1947. Inv. No. 457; Reg. No. 266.

Created K.G. in 1543; Earl of Wiltshire in 1549/50 and Marquess of Winchester
in 1551; Lord Treasurer of England during the reigns of Edward VI, Mary, and
Elizabeth.

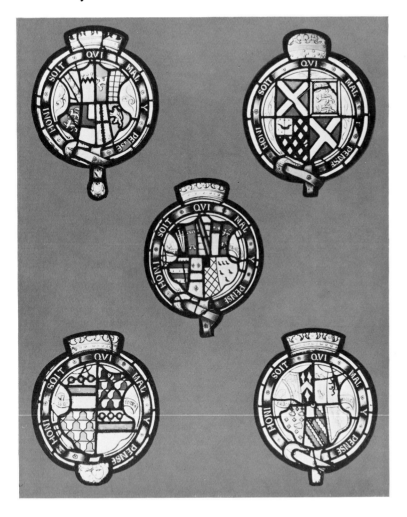

167 Circular garter medallion ensigned by a coronet with the shaped shield of SIR WALTER DEVEREUX, 3rd BARON FERRERS OF CHARTLEY, K.G. *(Devereux quartering Ferrers);* on either side of shield a scroll inscribed: lorde feres; pot metal; abrasion; yellow stain; $16\frac{1}{2} \times 13\frac{1}{2}$ in. 16th Century. Ex Coll: Vale Royal (Saloon, west window). Lit: The Genealogist, XXXVIII, 1921-2, 70. Acquired per Drake, 1947. Inv. No. 458; Reg. No. 45.267.

Grandson of Sir Walter Devereux by Anne, only daughter and heir of William Baron Ferrers of Chartley; created K.G. in 1523; Viscount Hereford in 1550; died in 1558. The inscription suggests a date prior to 1550 when he became Viscount Hereford. The third quarter is a restoration.

168 Circular quarter medallion ensigned by a coronet with shaped shield of WILLIAM HERBERT, later EARL OF PEMBROKE. *(1) and (7) Herbert; (2) Morgan; (3) Gamme; (4) Ashley; (5) Cradock; (6) Horton; at fess point a crescent or);* on either side of the shield a scroll inscribed: lorde herbert; pot metal; abrasion; yellow stain; $16\frac{3}{4} \times 13\frac{1}{4}$ in. 16th Century. Ex Coll: Vale Royal (Saloon, west window). Lit: The Genealogist, XXXVIII, 1921-2, 71. Acquired per Drake, 1947. Inv. No. 459; Reg. No. 45.268.

Created K.G. in 1549 and Earl of Pembroke in 1551; married, before 1534, Anne daughter of Sir Thomas Parr of Kendal, sister of Catherine Parr, last wife of Henry VIII. For the arms of her brother see no. 152. The inscription suggests a date prior to 1551 when he became 1st Earl of Pembroke.

169 Oval wreathed medallion with shaped shield probably for BOOTH, of Dunham Massey, Cheshire *(1) and (4) Massey; (2) Ashton quartering Stayley; (3) Fitton quartering Thornton);* scroll inscribed: Bothe of . . . . . . ; pot metal; abrasion; yellow stain; $17\frac{1}{4} \times 12\frac{1}{4}$ in. 16th Century. Ex Coll: Vale Royal (Saloon, east window). Lit: The Genealogist, XXXVIII, 1921-2, 78. Acquired per Drake, 1947. Inv. No. 460; Reg. No. 45.269.

Perhaps for George Boothe who died in 1543, but the arms of Boothe *(argent three boars heads erect and erased sable)* are omitted.

170 Oval wreathed medallion with the shaped shield of SIR WILLIAM VENABLES, titular Baron of Kinderton *(1) Venables; (2) Golborne; (3) Moston; (4) Ecleston; an escutcheon of pretence for Cotton);* pot metal; yellow stain; 17½ × 12¼ in. 16th Century. Ex Coll: Vale Royal (Saloon, east window). Lit: The Genealogist, XXXVIII, 1921-2, 80. Acquired per Drake, 1947. Inv. No. 462; Reg. No. 45.271. (See colour repro. p. 44).

Born 1491; Sheriff of Chester, 1526; married Elinor Cotton; died 1540.

171 Oval wreathed medallion with the shaped shield of SIR ROLAND STANLEY *(argent on a bend azure three bucks' heads cabossed or);* inscribed on scroll: Sir Roland Standley; pot metal; yellow stain; 13½ × 11½ in. 16th Century. Ex Coll: Vale Royal. Acquired per Drake 1947. Inv. No. 461; Reg. No. 45.270.

Not listed in The Genealogist (op. cit.).

172 Oval wreathed medallion with the straight-sided shield of HENRY RADCLIFFE, 4th EARL OF SUSSEX *(1) Fitzwalter; (2) Radcliffe; (3) Burnell, of Acton Burnell; (4) Botetourt; (5) Lucy; (6) Multon, of Egremont; (7) Mortimer, of Attleborough; (8) Culcheth, of Culcheth);* inscribed on scroll; therle of Sussex; pot metal; abrasion; yellow stain; 16¾ × 12¾ in. 16th Century. Ex Coll: Vale Royal (Saloon, east window). Lit: The Genealogist, XXXVIII, 1921-2, 82. Acquired per Drake, 1947. Inv. No. 463; Reg. No. 45.272.

K.G. 1554; died 1557; a book stamp with identically quartered shield is described by Cyril Davenport in English Heraldic Book-stamps (1909), p. 317 as that of Robert Radcliffe, 5th Earl of Sussex (b. *c.* 1550; d. 1629), only son of the above. The 4th, 6th and 7th quarters are said to be for Harding, Grey and Bereford.

173 Oval wreathed medallion with the shaped shield of SIR WILLIAM BRERETON *(1) argent two bars sable for Brereton; (2) Malpas; (3) ? Bruen; (4) Lestrange for Orreby);* inscribed on scroll: Sir William Brereton; pot metal; abrasion; yellow stain; 16¾ × 12¼ in. 16th Century. Ex Coll: Vale Royal (Saloon, east window). Lit: The Genealogist, XXXVIII, 1921-2, 76. Acquired per Drake, 1947. Inv. No. 464; Reg. No. 45.273.

Perhaps for Sir William Brereton, of Brereton, High Sheriff of Cheshire in 1548 and 1552.

174 Shield with the arms of CULCHETH, quarterly of eight *(1) Rait; (2) Culcheth; (3) Hartford; (4) De Vere; (5) Culcheth; (6) ? Haleth; (7) Jennying; (8) Heseltine)*; pot metal; abrasion; yellow stain; $8\frac{1}{4} \times 6\frac{7}{8}$ in. 16th Century. Ex Coll: Vale Royal. Acquired per Drake, 1947. Inv. No. 477; Reg. No. 45.286.

Not listed in The Genealogist (op. cit.), but labelled by Drake " Vale Royal 35."

175 Oval wreathed medallion with the straight-sided shield of SIR JOHN HARING-TON *(1) Harington, of Exton, co. Rutland; (2) Culpeper; (3) ? Beauchamp; (4) Hawte; (5) Hardreshull; (6) Bruce; (7) De La Launde; (8) ? Clifton)*; inscribed on scroll: Sir John Harington; pot metal; abrasion; yellow stain; $16\frac{3}{4} \times 12\frac{1}{4}$ in. 16th Century. Ex Coll: Vale Royal (Saloon, east window). Lit: The Genealogist, XXXVIII, 1921-2, 83. Acquired per Drake, 1947. Inv. No. 465; Reg. No. 45.274.

Probably for John Harington, Treasurer of the Camps and Buildings of Henry VIII and father of Sir John Harrington of Kelston, author of Nugae Antiquae, who commanded a troop of horse in Ireland under the Earl of Essex.

176 Shield with the arms of SIR HENRY CARY, BARON HUNSDON *(1) Cary; (2) Spencer; (3) Beaufort; (4) Beauchamp; (5) Newburgh (Warwick); (6) Berkeley; (7) Delisle; (8) Boleyn; (9) Hoo (Perrers); (10) Butler; (11) Segrave (Burnell); (12) St. Omer (Haversham); (13) Malmain; (14) Newman; (15) Talmage; (16) Hankford)*; yellow stain; enamel; $10\frac{5}{8} \times 9\frac{3}{4}$ in. 16th Century. Acquired per Drake, 1948. Inv. No. 483; Reg. No. 45.288.

Sir Henry Cary, son of William Cary by Lady Mary Boleyn (sister of Queen Anne Boleyn) was created Baron Hunsdon at the Coronation of Queen Elizabeth in 1559. He became Lord Chamberlain of the Household and died at Somerset House in 1596.

177 Panel with the shaped shield of MINSHULL, of Erdeswick *(azure a crescent between three sunbursts argent)*; inscribed " armes de meschall "; pot metal; yellow stain; $10\frac{1}{2} \times 8$ in. 16th Century. Ex Coll: Utkinton Hall; Tarporley Rectory (staircase window); Vale Royal. Lit: The Genealogist, XXXVIII, 1921-2, 19. Inv. No. 469; Reg. No. 45.278. (See colour repro. p. 44).

Recorded by Cole, 1755 (B.M. Add. MS. 5830, ink f. 43); listed as " not at Vale Royal " in Genealogist (op. cit.), but labelled by Drake " Vale Royal 27."

178 Panel with the shaped shield of BERESFORD *(argent a bear salient sable muzzled, collared and chained or)* quartering HASSALL *) per chevron argent and or three pheons and in chief a crescent sable);* inscribed on scroll: Beyresford; pot metal; yellow stain; $11\frac{1}{4} \times 8\frac{5}{8}$ in. 16th Century. Acquired per Drake, 1948. Inv. No. 485; Reg. No. 45.290.

Possibly from Vale Royal but not listed as such.

179 Panel with the shaped shield of WILBRAHAM, of Woodhey *(azure two bars argent on a canton sable a wolf's head erased within a bordure of the second);* pot metal; yellow stain; $10 \times 7\frac{1}{4}$ in. 16th Century. Ex Coll: Utkinton Hall; Tarporley Rectory (west chamber); Vale Royal. Lit: The Genealogist, XXXVIII, 1921-2, 16. Acquired per Drake, 1947. Inv. No. 470; Reg. No. 45.279. (See colour repro. p. 44).

Recorded by Cole, 1755 (B.M. Add. MS. 5830, ink f. 43) as bearing the inscription " armes de Wellbrunne " under the shield; listed as " not at Vale Royal " in the Genealogist (op. cit.), but labelled by Drake " Vale Royal 28."

180 Panel with the shaped shield of HOLFORD, of Holford *(argent a greyhound passant sable);* yellow stain ; $10\frac{1}{4} \times 7\frac{1}{4}$ in. 16th Century. Ex Coll: Utkinton Hall; Tarporley Rectory (in little lower room through kitchen); Vale Royal (Entrance Hall, east window). Lit: The Genealogist, XXXVIII, 1921-2, 25 and 51. Acquired per Drake, 1947. Inv. No. 474; Reg. No. 45.283.

Recorded by Cole, 1755 (B.M. Add. MS. 5830, ink f. 44) as the arms of " Holford, a Cheshire family (of) good antiquity." The mother of Thomas Cholmondeley (1595-1653), who acquired Vale Royal in 1616, was a Holford.

181 Panel with the helm, mantling, crest *(a buck's head cabossed gules),* supporters *(dexter a talbot sable, sinister a talbot argent)* and shield *(azure two bars argent, on a bend gules three arrows of the second)* of JOHN DONE, of Flaxyards and Utkinton; yellow stain and enamel; $7 \times 5$ in. 16th/17th Century. Ex Coll: Utkinton Hall; Tarporley Rectory (in servant's bedroom); ? Vale Royal. Lit: The Genealogist, XXXVIII, 1921-2, 6. Original Gift; ex Hutton Castle, 1962. Inv. No. 126; Reg. No. 45.210. (See also repro. p. 7).

One of the seven small " modern " shields recorded by Cole in 1755 (B.M. Add. MS. 5830, ink f. 40); listed as " not at Vale Royal " in The Genealogist (op. cit.). John Done, 13th Master Forester in Delamere Forest (1591-1601) married his cousin Ellen, daughter and heiress of James Done of Utkinton. His son was knighted by James I at Utkinton in 1617.

# Vale Royal

Cat. No. 154

Cat. No. 170

Cat. No. 189

Cat. No. 177

Cat. No. 179

182 Shield of SIR JOHN DONE, of Utkinton *(azure two bars argent, on a bend gules three arrows of the second);* inscribed below the shield: Sir John Doune; pot metal; abrasion; yellow stain; $9\frac{1}{2} \times 7\frac{1}{2}$ in. 16th Century. Ex Coll: Spurstow Hall; Utkinton Hall; Tarporley Rectory (Mr. Allen's Chamber); ? Vale Royal. Lit: The Genealogist, XXXVIII, 1921-2, 13. Original Gift; ex Hutton Castle, 1956. Inv. No. 192; Reg. No. 45.224.

Probably one of the " very ancient " shields tricked in the hall window at Spurstowe Hall, 1599; recorded by Cole, 1755 (B.M. Add. MS. 5830, ink f. 42) as one of three ancient coats in Mr. Allen's chamber; listed in The Genealogist, XXXVIII as " not at Vale Royal." Sir John Done, 11th Master Forester (1516-1561) married Jane Mainwaring, who died in 1562 and was buried at Tarporley.

183 Panel with the shaped shield of RIDLEY, of Ridley *(argent a bull passant gules horned or standing in a green field);* inscribed below the shield: armes de Rodlay; pot metal; abrasion; yellow stain; $13\frac{1}{2} \times 10\frac{1}{2}$ in. 16th Century. Ex Coll: Spurstow Hall; Utkinton Hall; Tarporley Rectory (Mr. Allen's Chamber); Vale Royal (Saloon, east window). Lit: The Genealogist, XXXVIII, 1921-2, 12, 36, 85. Acquired per Drake, 1947. Inv. No. 466; Reg. No. 45.275.

The shield is tricked with a stag above the words " arma de Rodley " in the Spurstow drawing (B.M. Harl. MS. 2151, f. 167); recorded by Cole, 1755 (B.M. Add. MS. 5830, ink f. 42) who comments " under them (the arms) is wrote " armes de Rodlay." This coat belongs to the name of Ridley." According to Ormerod, History of Cheshire, Vol. II, p. 297, who saw the shield at Vale Royal, there were Ridleys at Tarporley in the time of Queen Elizabeth.

184 Quarry with the crest of RIDLEY *(a white bull chained or);* yellow stain; $6\frac{1}{2} \times 4\frac{3}{8}$ in 16th Century. Original Gift; ex Hutton Castle, 1948. Inv. No. 170; Reg. No. 45.214.

185 Panel with the shield of ARDERN, of Harden *(gules three crosses crosslet fitchee and a chief or)*; shield in ornamental surround; yellow stain and enamel; 6×5 in. 16th/17th Century. Ex Coll: Tarporley Rectory (servant's bedroom); ? Vale Royal. Lit: The Genealogist, XXXVIII, 1921-2, 2. Acquired per Drake, 1947. Inv. No. 129; Reg. No. 45.340.

Probably another of the small "modern" shields recorded by Cole, 1755 (B.M. Add. MS. 5830 ink f. 40). Another of these seven small shields, recorded by Cole but not in the Burrell Collection, showed Ardern impaling Done (Eleanor, daughter and co-heiress of Sir John Done of Utkinton married Ralph Ardern and inherited Utkinton). Listed in The Genealogist (op. cit.) as "not at Vale Royal."

186 Oval medallion with the shaped shield of CHOLMONDELEY *(gules two esquires helmets in chief proper in base a garb or)*; inscribed: armes de chomlay; pot metal; abrasion; yellow stain; 13¾×11¾ in. 16th Century. Ex Coll: Spurstow Hall; ? Utkinton Hall; Tarporley Rectory (Mr. Allen's Chamber); Vale Royal (Saloon, west window). Lit: The Genealogist, XXXVIII, 1921-2, 12, 43, 66. Acquired per Drake, 1947. Inv. No. 471; Reg. No. 45.280.

Tricked under the inscription in the Spurstow drawing; listed by Cole with the Donne and Ridley arms in Mr. Allen's room (see Nos. 182 and 183). Probably for Sir Hugh Cholmondeley of Cholmondeley (d. 1596). These are the arms of the present Lord Delamere of Vale Royal. The pale yellow oval surround is a later addition.

187 Shaped shield of SPURSTOW *(vert three pierced mullets or)* quartering BULKELEY for NORBURY, of Frodsham *(sable on a chevron between three bulls' heads cabossed argent, a crescent for difference)*; pot metal; yellow stain; 9½×8½ in. 16th Century. Ex Coll: Spurstow Hall; ? Utkinton Hall; Tarporley Rectory (staircase window); Vale Royal (Entrance Hall, east window). Lit: The Genealogist, XXXVIII, 1921-2, 38, 21, 48. Acquired per Drake, 1947. Inv. No. 473; Reg. No.45.282.

In the Spurstow Hall tricking the shield is surmounted by helm, mantling, wreath and crest *(a woman's head couped below the shoulders, hair flowing)* between the letters I.S.; one of the six shields listed by Cole, 1755 (ink f. 42) as being in the staircase window at Tarporley of which two others are in the Collection (see nos. 177, 188). George Spurstow (d. 1603) married Alice, daughter and co-heiress of John Norbury (the Norburys derived from a Bulkeley cadet and had assumed the Bulkeley arms).

188 Oval medallion with the shaped shield of STARKEY *(argent a stork close sable, beaked legged and charged on the breast with a crescent or)* quartering OULTON *(quarterly azure, sic for vert, and gules a lion rampant argent)*; pot metal; yellow stain; 14¾×12½ in. 16th Century. Ex Coll: ? Utkinton Hall; Tarporley Rectory (staircase window); Vale Royal (Saloon, east window). Lit: The Genealogist, XXXVIII, 1921-2, 20, 77. Acquired per Drake, 1947. Inv. No. 472; Reg. No. 45.281.

Hugh Starkey, son of Peter Starkey, of Stretton, and Joan de Oulton, married Elinor, daughter of John Done of Utkinton. The pink oval surround is a later addition.

189 Shaped shield of THELWALL *(gules on a chevron between three boars' heads couped argent three trefoils slipped sable)*; pot metal; abrasion; 8½×6¾ in. 16th Century. Ex Coll: Vale Royal. Acquired per Drake, 1947. Inv. No. 476; Reg. No. 45.285. (See colour repro. p. 44).

Not listed in the Genealogist, XXXVIII, but labelled by Drake "Vale Royal 34". Thelwall is noted by Camden (Britannia, 1695, p. 560) as an obscure village but formerly a large city deriving its name from the wall of tree trunks (Anglo-Saxon Dele) with which it was surrounded.

190 Panel with the shaped shield of BRERETON, of Malpas *(argent two bars sable on the upper a crescent argent)* quartering IPSTONES *(argent a chevron between three crescents gules)*; inscribed: brereto amalpas; pot metal; abrasion; yellow stain; 13½×9½ in. 16th Century. Ex Coll: Spurstow Hall; ? Utkinton Hall; Tarporley Rectory (Mr. Cole's bedroom); Vale Royal (Saloon, east window). Lit: The Genealogist, XXXVIII, 1921-2, 35, 10, 84. Acquired per Drake, 1947. Inv. No. 467; Reg. No. 45.276.

Tricked in the Spurstow Hall drawing under the inscription: B: de Malpasse. The Breretons of Malpas and Ipstones were a younger branch of the Breretons of Brereton. The shield may be for Sir Randle Brereton, of Malpas (living 1566).

191 Shield of BERLINGHAM *(barry of six gules and argent)*; pot metal; 9½×8½ in. 16th Century. Ex Coll: Vale Royal. Acquired per Drake, 1947. Inv. No. 475; Reg. No. 45.284.

Not listed in the Genealogist, XXXVIII, but labelled by Drake "Vale Royal 33". The arms are closely related to those of Manwaring *(argent two bars gules)* for whom Cole noted three separate shields at Tarporley Rectory in 1755.

192  Panel with the shaped shield of VENABLES of Kinderton *(azure two bars argent)*; inscribed below the shield: armes de Kenderton; pot metal; yellow stain; 13×9 in. 16th Century. Ex Coll: Spurstow Hall; Tarporley Rectory (Mr. Cole's bedroom); Vale Royal (Saloon, east window). Lit: The Genealogist, XXXVIII, 1921-2, 41, 9, 74. Acquired per Drake, 1947. Inv. No. 468; Reg. No. 45.277.

Tricked in the Spurstow Hall drawing under the words " armes de Kenderton " and noted by Cole (ink f. 41) as " one of the four very old coats in the chamber where I lay," another being No. 190. Probably for Sir Thomas Venables, titular baron of Kinderton (knighted 1544, died 1580).

193  Roundel with shaped shield ensigned by a crown bearing the Red Rose of LAN-CASTER *(argent a rose gules barbed and seeded or slipped vert)*; yellow stain border with grotesque beasts; pot metal; yellow stain; 17¼×14 in. 16th Century. Ex Coll: Cowick Priory, Devon; A. L. Radford (Bradninch Manor). Original Gift; ex Hutton Castle, 1956. Inv. No. 5; Reg. No. 45.180.

This or the following (no. 194) is probably the " crowned rose of Henry VIII, from Cowick " lent to the Victoria and Albert Museum, London, by Mr. A. L. Radford in 1915.

194  Roundel with shaped shield ensigned by a crown bearing the Red and White Rose of LANCASTER AND YORK *(argent a rose argent surrounded by a rose gules seeded and barbed or slipped vert)*; yellow stain border with winged heads and grotesque beasts; pot metal; yellow stain; 19¼×14 in. 16th Century. Ex Coll: Cowick Priory; A. L. Radford (Bradninch Manor). Original Gift; ex Hutton Castle 1956. Inv. No. 6; Reg. No. 45.181.

195  Roundel with shaped shield ensigned by a prince's coronet bearing the arms of the PRINCE OF WALES, afterwards Edward VI *(France and England quarterly, a label of three points argent)*; yellow stain border with grotesque beasts; pot metal; abrasion; yellow stain; dia. 14 in. 16th Century. Ex Coll: Cowick Priory; A. L. Radford (Bradninch Manor). Original Gift; ex Hutton Castle, 1956. Inv. No. 7; Reg. No. 45.182.

Probably the " arms of Edward VI as Prince of Wales, from Cowick " lent to the Victoria and Albert Museum, London, by Mr. A. L. Radford in 1915.

196 Roundel with shaped shield for PRINCE OF WALES, afterwards Edward VI
*(France and England quarterly, a label of three points argent);* yellow stain border with
winged heads, cupids and bearded warriors; pot metal; abrasion; yellow stain;
dia. 17⅛ in. 16th Century. Ex Coll: Cowick Priory; A. L. Radford (Bradninch
Manor). Original Gift; ex Hutton Castle, 1956. Inv. No. 8; Reg. No. 45.183.

197 Roundel with shaped shield of HENRY VIII AND JANE SEYMOUR *(dexter:
France and England; sinister (1) Seymour augmentations (2) Seymour; (3) Beauchamp;
(4) Esturmy; (5) MacWilliam; (6) Coker)* within a rose border containing alter-
nately red and white roses and the initials H.R.; pot metal; abrasion; yellow
stain; dia. 16 in. 16th Century. Ex Coll: Richard Cockle Lucas; A. L. Radford.
Original Gift; ex Hutton Castle, 1956. Inv. No. 9; Reg. No. 45.184.

This and the three following medallions probably derive from the " great treasure
trove of ancient art " acquired by R. C. Lucas, the sculptor, who became
posthumously famous when a bust of Flora, bought by the Berlin Museum as a work
by Leonardo da Vinci was declared to be his creation. He used the stained glass
which he believed to have come from Nonsuch Palace to adorn a house which he
built near Chilworth (see An Account of a Residence designed and built by R. C.
Lucas, Sculptor, 1854). A similar roundel with the arms of Henry VIII and Jane
Seymour within a chaplet of red and white roses from the Lucas and Radford
Collections was acquired by the Victoria and Albert Museum, London (reproduced
as frontispiece to A History of English Glass-Painting by Maurice Drake, 1912).

198 Roundel with shaped and scrolling shield of PRINCE OF WALES, afterwards
Edward VI *(France and England quarterly with label of three points argent)* within a
running rose border of alternating red and white roses and the initials E.P.; pot
metal; abrasion; yellow stain; dia. 16 in. 16th Century. Ex Coll: R. C. Lucas;
A. L. Radford. Original Gift; ex Hutton Castle, 1956. Inv. No. 10, Reg. No.
45.185.

The second quarter is restored.

199 Roundel with straight-sided shield ensigned by a crown with the ROYAL ARMS
OF ENGLAND *(France and England quarterly);* oak leaf border with sunburst;
pot metal; abrasion; yellow stain; 19¼ × 15½ in. 16th Century. Ex Coll: R. C.
Lucas; A. L. Radford. Original Gift; ex Hutton Castle, 1956. Inv. No. 11;
Reg. No. 45.186.

The fleurs de lys in the first and fourth quarters are yellow stained on the pale
blue glass; in nos. 197, 198 and 200 the fleurs de lys are inserted, while the lions
are abraded.

200 Roundel with hour-glass shaped shield ensigned by a crown with the ROYAL ARMS OF ENGLAND *(France and England quarterly)* within a wreath of leaves red and white roses, and the initials H. R. in monogram; pot metal, abrasion; yellow stain; $19\frac{3}{4} \times 15\frac{1}{2}$ in. 16th Century. Ex Coll: R. C. Lucas; A. L. Radford. Original Gift; ex Hutton Castle, 1956. Inv. No. 12; Reg. No. 45.187.

201 Oval medallion with badge of HENRY VIII *(a portcullis or)* ensigned by a royal crown and enclosed by a wreath of oak leaves and red roses; pot metal; yellow stain; $17\frac{1}{2} \times 12\frac{1}{2}$ in. 16th Century. Ex Coll: Hearst, New York. Original Gift; ex Hutton Castle. Inv. No. 295; Reg. No. 45.234.

A gold portcullis was used by both Henry VII and Henry VIII as a badge with the motto " altera securitas " (possibly deriving from a pun on the name Tudor i.e. two-door, but Fox-Davies (Heraldic Badges, 1907, p. 53) notes that it was also used by the Beauforts who had no Tudor descent).

202 Four quarries: *(a)* the initial W. and the monogram P. L. joined by a loveknot issuing from a flower and heart and terminating in two sea-shells; yellow stain; $6\frac{1}{2} \times 5\frac{1}{4}$ in. 16th Century. Acquired 1948. Inv. No. 493; Reg. No. 45.107.

*(b)* and *(c)* Badge of COURTENAY, co. Devon *(a dolphin embowed)*; yellow stain; $6\frac{1}{4} \times 4\frac{5}{8}$ in. 16th Century. Original Gift; ex Hutton Castle. Inv. Nos. 288 and 289; Reg. Nos. 45.163 and 164.

*(d)* Fetterlock badge; yellow stain; $5\frac{3}{4} \times 4\frac{1}{2}$ in. 16th Century. Ex Coll: Sir Hercules Read, F.S.A. Exhibited: B.F.A.C. British Heraldic Art, 1916, p. 119, No. 9. Original Gift; ex Hutton Castle, 1948. Inv. No. 169; Reg. No. 45.213.

A Fetterlock badge is attributed to Arthur, Prince of Wales (son of Henry VII); Richard Plantagenet (d. 1460), Duke of York; and Henry Bourchier (d. 1483), Earl of Essex.

203 Oval medallion with badge of HENRY VIII AND JANE SEYMOUR *(a fleur de lys on two wings conjoined in lure or)* ensigned by a crown and within a border similar to no. 201; pot metal; yellow stain; $17\frac{1}{2} \times 11\frac{3}{4}$ in. 16th Century. Ex Coll: Hearst, New York. Original Gift; ex Hutton Castle. Inv. No. 296; Reg. No. 45.235. (See colour repro. p. 68).

204 Roundel with the ROSE OF YORK *(sable a rose argent seeded or)* within a black border studded with yellow; yellow stain; dia. 6¼ in. 16th Century. Ex Coll: A. L. Radford (Bovey House). Original Gift; ex Hutton Castle. Inv. No. 250; Reg. No. 45.162.

On the rose is scratched: Peter Cole glazier made all ye heads of these windows 1765. It was on loan to the Victoria and Albert Museum, London, in 1915.

205 Large quarry comprising four smaller quarries: *(a)* crowned initial R. perhaps for RICHARD III; *(b)* a white hart lodged perhaps for RICHARD II; *(c)* the white lion of March for the DUKE OF YORK; *(d)* the plantagenista and initials h.B. perhaps for HARRY BROME (Bolingbroke); yellow stain; 11×9 in. 16th Century. Ex Coll: Sir Henry Ellis; Sir Hercules Read, F.S.A. (sold Sotheby's, 9.11.28, lots 714-5). Exhibited: B.F.A.C. British Heraldic Art, 1916, p. 120, No. 11 pl. XXVI (quarry with the white lion cf March). Original Gift; ex Hutton Castle, 1956. Inv. No. 183; Reg. No. 45.219.

According to Sotheby's sale catalogue these quarries formed part of a collection made by Sir Henry Ellis to illustrate a series of letters read at the Society of Antiquaries in 1822 on royal badges (see also nos. 207 and 209), but there is no trace of any such letters in Archaeologia.

206 Roundel with the monogram L.T. within a spiral leaf border; yellow stain; dia 7⅜ in. 16th Century. Ex Coll: Eumorfopoulos. Original Gift; ex Hutton Castle. Inv. No. 252; Reg. No. 45.70.

207 Large quarry comprising four small quarries: *(a)* crowned initial R. perhaps for RICHARD III; *(b)* and *(c)* crowned fleur-de-lys between the initials E. and R. perhaps for EDWARD VI; *(d)* the plantagenista between the initials h.B. perhaps for HARRY BROME (Bolingbroke); yellow stain; 12½×10 in. 16th Century. Ex Coll: Sir Henry Ellis; Sir Hercules Read, F.S.A. Original Gift; ex Hutton Castle, 1956. Inv. No. 185; Reg. No. 45.220. See nos. 205 and 209.

208 Roundel with the Sacred Monogram I H C crowned; yellow stain; dia. 7¾ in. 16th Century. Ex Coll: Eumorfopoulos. Acquired per Drake, 1944; ex Hutton Castle, 1948. Inv. No. 399; Reg. No. 45.80.

209 Large quarry comprising four small quarries: *(a)* the Bosworth thornbush enfiling a royal crown with the initials H. and E. perhaps for HENRY VII and ELIZABETH OF YORK; *(b)* and *(c)* the plantagenista (broom-plant) perhaps for HARRY BROME (Bolingbroke); *(d)* a crowned rose of York; yellow stain; 12×9¼ in. 16th Century. Ex Coll: Sir Henry Ellis; Sir Hercules Read, F.S.A. Exhibited: B.F.A.C. British Heraldic Art, 1916, p. 119, No. 4. Original Gift; ex Hutton Castle, 1956. Inv. No. 186; Reg. No. 45.221. See also nos. 205 and 207.

210 Roundel with the monogram H. R. or H. B. within a spiral leaf border similar to No. 206; yellow stain; dia. 7¾ in. 16th Century. Ex Coll: Eumorfopoulos. Acquired per Drake, 1944; ex Hutton Castle, 1948. Inv. No. 400; Reg. No. 45.81.

211 Panel with roundel containing the monogram W. B.; yellow stain; 12¾×12⅜ in. 16th Century. Ex Coll: Sir Hercules Read, F.S.A. Original Gift; ex Hutton Castle, 1956. Inv. No. 167; Reg. No. 45.211.

    Sold with no. 213 as lot 710 at Sotheby, 9.11.28; the initials are for William BRADBRIDGE, Bishop of Exeter, 1571-8.

212 Large quarry comprising four small quarries each with the rayed monogram J. S.; yellow stain; 12×9¼ in. 16th Century. Original Gift; ex Hutton Castle, 1956. Inv. No. 184; Reg. No. 45.158.

213 Panel with roundel containing the shield of the DIOCESE OF EXETER *(argent two keys addorsed in saltire, in pale a sword up-pointed)* and on either side the initial R. and the monogram I. S.; yellow stain; 12¾×12¼ in. 16th Century. Ex Coll: Sir Hercules Read, F.S.A. Orignial Gift; ex Hutton Castle, 1956. Inv. No. 168; Reg. No. 45.212. See no. 211.

214 Roundel with the Eagle, symbol of ST. JOHN THE EVANGELIST, perched on the Book of Revelation, with inscribed scroll: In principio erat verbum et verbu erat; yellow stain; dia. 8⅛ in. 15th Century. Original Gift; ex Hutton Castle, 1956. Inv. No. 106; Reg. No. 45.61.

215 Large quarry with the rebus of JOHN ISLIP (d. 1532), Abbot of Westminster *(a man slipping from a tree clutching a severed branch, i.e. slip, between the representation of an eye and the word SLIP)*; yellow stain; $12 \times 9\frac{1}{2}$ in. 16th Century. Lit: Tanner, Scottish Art Review, 1962, Vol. VIII, No. 4. Original Gift: ex Hutton Castle, 1956. Inv. No. 191; Reg. No. 45.223.

Perhaps painted for the Chantry Chapel of Abbot Islip in Westminster Abbey, or some other part of the abbey " in the windows whereof (saith Camden) he had a quadruple device for his single name; for somewhere he set up an eye with a slip of a tree; in other places an I with the said slip; and in some places one slipping from the tree with the word Islip " (J. Weever, Ancient Funerall Monuments, 1631, p. 488). A carved stone head, believed to represent John Islip, the last of the great abbots of Westminster, is preserved in the abbey (Lit: Tanner, Westminster Abbey Quarterly, 1939, Vol. I, No. 1). Some other examples of the Islip rebus in stained glass are discussed by F. Sydney Eden in The Connoisseur, April, 1924, p. 204.

216 Roundel with the Eagle, symbol of ST. JOHN THE EVANGELIST, perched on a mound with an inscribed scroll issuing from its beak: In deo te confido; yellow stain; dia. $8\frac{1}{8}$ in. 15th Century. Original Gift; ex Hutton Castle, 1956. Inv. No. 107; Reg. No. 45.62.

217 Panel comprising thirteen quarries, some identified as badges, lettered *(a)*, *(b)* and *(c)* three plant sprigs including the Rose and Columbine for HENRY IV; *(d)* and *(e)* portcullis for HENRY VII and VIII; *(f)*, *(g)* and *(h)* two plants and the burial of Reynard the Fox; *(j)* a white falcon gorged with a ducal coronet for RICHARD II; *(k)* and *(l)* the rose-en-soleil for EDWARD IV; *(m)* a flower with eight petals; *(n)* ears of barley, said to be for WYDVILLE; yellow stain; $22\frac{1}{8} \times 16\frac{3}{4}$ in. 16th Century. Original Gift; ex Hutton Castle. Inv. No. 334; Reg. No. 45.102.

218 Panel with thistle, perhaps for SCOTLAND (but not crowned); yellow stain; $5\frac{3}{4} \times 5$ in. 16th Century. Original Gift; ex Hutton Castle. Inv. No. 263; Reg. No. 45.228.

CARVED REBUS on the cornice of the Islip Chapel.
*Westminster Abbey*

219 Panel comprising thirteen quarries, some identified as badges and crests, lettered *(o)* a griffin's head erased; *(p)* a running man-headed tiger; *(q)* an eagle's head guttee de larmes erased holding a flower sprig in its beak, said to be for WALCOT; *(r)* a stork; *(s)* a panther passant, perhaps for HENRY VI; *(t)* rebus of WILLIAM MIDDLETON, a bird perched on a barrel with inscribed scroll: W. Middil-t-un, and the black letter " t " between; *(u)* a stag statant surrounded by the letters A. I. B. C. ff. and p., said to be the rebus of BUCKLAND; *(v)* similar to *(t)* above; *(w)* and *(x)* two birds; *(y)* the initials h. and p. joined by a chain; *(z)* bird and merchant's mark; *(zz)* a demi-bull, rampant or, said to be for BULMER; yellow stain; $22\frac{1}{8} \times 16\frac{1}{2}$ in. 16th Century. Original Gift; ex Hutton Castle. Inv. No. 334; Reg. No. 45.102.

220 Oval medallion with the shield of MALTRAVERS *(sable a fret or)* in a cartouche surrounded by ornamental swags of fruit, naked boys, animals, birds and insects; yellow stain and enamel; 21¼ × 15 in. Late 16th Century. Original Gift; ex Hutton Castle, 1956. Inv. No. 58; Reg. No. 45.193.

This and the three following medallions came from the chapel at Compton Verney, Warwickshire. They were sold at Christie's 30.7.1931 (lots 123 and 133). Numerous related panels and medallions from the same chapel were in 1946 with the Hearst Collection at St. Donat's Castle.

221 Oval medallion with the shield of TALBOT *(1) Talbot; (2) Tibetot; (3) Charlton; (4) Somery; (5) Segrave; (6) Maltravers; (7) Tibetot impaling Charlton; (8) Tibetot; (9) Strange impaling Neville)* in a cartouche and ornamental surround similar to nos. 220, 222 and 223; pot metal; abrasion; yellow stain; enamel; 21¼ × 14¾ in. Late 16th Century. Original Gift; ex Hutton Castle, 1956. Inv. No. 59; Reg. No. 45.194.

222 Oval medallion with the shield of DUDLEY *(or a lion rampant double quivee vert, a mullet for difference, quartering Botreux, Monthermer, Boughton, and impaling Bacon, Blayney, Dudley and Charlton)* in a cartouche and surround similar to nos. 220, 221 and 223; pot metal; abrasion; yellow stain; enamel; 21½ × 15¼ in. Late 16th Century. Original Gift; ex Hutton Castle, 1956. Inv. No. 60; Reg. No. 45.195.

223 Oval medallion with the shield of STAFFORD *(or a chevron gules within a bordure engrailed sable)* in a cartouche and surround similar to nos. 220, 221 and 222; pot metal; yellow stain; enamel; 21¼ × 15¼ in. Late 16th Century. Original Gift; ex Hutton Castle, 1956. Inv. No. 61; Reg. No. 45.196.

224 Oval medallion with the helm, mantling *(argent and or)*, crest *(a talbot's head erased sable)* and shield *(sable a griffin segreant argent)* of EDWARD GRIFFIN BENE-FACTOR *(thus inscribed on scroll beneath shield)*; yellow stain; enamel; 16½ × 12½ in. 17th Century. Acquired per Drake, 1948. Inv. No. 491; Reg. No. 45.360.

225 Shaped medallion with the shield of DAYRELL *(azure a lion rampant crowned or)* quartering AYLMER *(or a cross sable between four Cornish choughs proper)* impaling PUDSEY *(vert a chevron between three pierced mullets or)* quartering CAMDEN *(argent a fess engrailed between six crosses crosslet fitchy sable)* in a cartouche and floral wreath dated 1595; yellow stain and enamel; 13¾ × 10½ in. Late 16th Century. Ex Coll: Cote Manor House, co. Warwick. Acquired per Drake, 1946. Inv. No. 441; Reg. No. 45.251. (See colour repro. p. 68).

226 Oval medallion with the shield of COSYN *(ermine a chevron per pale or and sable)* in a cartouche embellished with fruit swags; yellow stain and enamel; 15½ × 11 in. Late 16th Century. Ex Coll: Cote Manor House, co. Warwick. Acquired per Drake, 1946. Inv. No. 440; Reg. No. 45.250.

227 Oval medallion with the helm, mantling *(argent and gules)*, crest *(dexter arm in armour embowed holding in the hand a tilting lance)* and shield of BLAYNEY *(1) sable three horses' heads erased argent quartering; (2) Chatterton; (3) Blayney of Montgomery; (4) Lewis; (5) Boughton; (6) Bradwen)* in a cartouche inscribed with motto and date: Fide ne Difide Ano 1584; pot enamel; abrasion; yellow stain; enamel; 22¼ × 15¾ in. Late 16th Century. Original Gift; ex Hutton Castle, 1956. Inv. No. 189; Reg. No. 45.222.

228 Oval medallion with the shield of ROBERT GEORGE, of Cirencester, co. Gloucester *(argent on a fess gules between two hawks volant sable a crescent or)* impaling Margaret, daughter of Richard OLDISWORTH *(gules on a fess argent three lions passant guardant purpure)* in a cartouche inscribed with the names above and the date "1599" below; pot metal; abrasion; yellow stain; enamel; 14 × 9½ in. Late 16th Century. Original Gift; ex Hutton Castle, 1956. Inv. No. 66; Reg. No. 45.201.

Painted for the Oldisworth family seat, Poltons Court, Gloucestershire. Her brother's arms are shown in No. 229.

229 Oval medallion with the shield of ARNOLD OLDISWORTH impaling Lucy, daughter of Francis BERRY *(or a griffin segreant sable)* in a cartouche inscribed with the names above and the date "1599" below; pot metal; abrasion; yellow stain; enamel; 14 × 9½ in. Late 16th Century. Original Gift; ex Hutton Castle, 1956. Inv. No. 67, Reg. No. 45.202.

Arnold Oldisworth was living in London in 1604.

230 Circular garter medallion ensigned by an earl's coronet with the shield of HASTINGS, EARL OF HUNTINGDON, K.G. *(1) Hastings; (2) Hungerford of Heytesbury; (3) Clarence; (4) Neville);* pot metal; abrasion; yellow stain; enamel; 22½ × 13¾ in. Early 17th Century. Ex Coll: Lord Bagot, Blithfield Hall, Staffs. Acquired per Drake, 1946. Inv. No. 432; Reg. No. 45.249.

Perhaps for Henry, 5th Earl Huntingdon (succeeded 1604).

231 Circular garter medallion ensigned by an earl's coronet with the shield of DEVEREUX, EARL OF ESSEX, K.G. *(1) Devereux; (2) Ferrers; (3) Bourchier; (4) Gloucester);* pot metal; abrasion; yellow stain; enamel; 23¼ × 14½ in. Early 17th Century. Ex Coll: Lord Bagot, Blithfield Hall, Staffs. Acquired per Drake, 1946. Inv. No. 431; Reg. No. 45.248.

Perhaps for Robert, 3rd Earl of Essex (succeeded 1601).

232 Circular garter medallion ensigned by an earl's coronet with the shield of TALBOT, EARL OF SHREWSBURY, K.G. *(1) Belesme; (2) Gloucester; (3) Neville; (4) Stanley);* pot metal; abrasion; yellow stain; enamel; 22½ × 13¾ in. Early 17th Century. Ex Coll: Lord Bagot, Blithfield Hall, Staffs. Acquired per Drake, 1946. Inv. No. 430; Reg. No. 45.247.

Perhaps for Gilbert, 7th Earl of Shrewsbury (succeeded 1590).

233 Circular garter medallion ensigned by a crown with the ROYAL ARMS *(1) and (4) France quartering England; (2) Scotland; (3) Ireland);* yellow stain; blue and some red enamel; 18¼ × 10½ in. Early 17th Century. Ex Coll: Lord Bagot, Blithfield Hall, Staffs. Acquired per Drake, 1946. Inv. No. 433; Reg. No. 45.355.

The Royal Arms as marshalled in England between the union of the crowns in 1603 and the union of the parliaments in 1707.

234 Oval medallion with the shield of SIR THOMAS WENTWORTH, K.B., 4th Baron Wentworth (later Earl of Cleveland) and Anne, daughter of SIR JOHN CROFTS *(Dexter: (1) Wentworth; (2) Despencer; (3) Clare; (4) Goushill (Mandeville); (5) Poynton (Fitzwarren); (6) Oyrey (Herring); (7) Tibetot; (8) Badlesmere; (9) Holland (Woodstock); (10) Neville; (11) Montagu; (12) Monthermer; (13) Fortescue; (14) Stonor (Delapoole); (15) Delapole; (16) Inglethorpe; (17) Bradstone; (18) Kirkby (Harnhull); (19) Harnehall; Sinister: Crofts quartering Sampson)* in a cartouche and laurel wreath with scroll inscribed: Lo. Wentworth and Crofts; yellow stain and enamel; $16\frac{1}{2} \times 12\frac{1}{2}$ in. Early 17th Century. Original Gift (acquired per Drake, 1942), ex Hutton Castle. Inv. No. 375; Reg. No. 45.352. (See also repro. p. 56).

Sir Thomas Wentworth (1591-1667) of Nettlestead, succeeded his father, the third lord, in 1593, and was knighted in 1610. He married, firstly, Anne (d. 1637/8), one of the seven daughters of Sir John Crofts, by Mary, daughter of Sir Thomas Shirley, before 1612. In 1614, he inherited the estate of Toddington in Bedfordshire and left his seat at Nettlestead to settle there. The Crofts were an old-established Suffolk family, of Saxham Parva and Wiston. The Wentworth quarterings as listed above are the same as those of the 2nd Lord Wentworth of Nettlestead (d. 1584) as they appear (with some variations in the order and the repetition of one) in a shield, quarterly of twenty, carved on the stone gateway of Nettlestead Hall (see W. L. Rutton, Three Branches of the Family of Wentworth, 1891). The names listed as alternative identifications in brackets are those given in the Burrell Inventory (presumably by Drake). This and the six following medallions are from Saxham Hall, the seat of the Croft family in Suffolk. They were acquired by Grosvenor Thomas and Drake from Dr. Philip Nelson. Another (Crofts impaling Poley) was acquired by the Melbourne Art Gallery, Australia. No. 234 is reproduced in The Loyal Wentworths by Allan Fea, 1928, opposite page 74.

235 Oval medallion with the shield of JOHN CROFTS *(or three bulls' heads cabossed sable)* impaling COCKETT *(per bend argent and sable on a bend three fleurs de lys all counterchanged and a crescent or for difference)* in a cartouche and laurel wreath with inscribed scroll; yellow stain and enamel; $17 \times 12\frac{1}{2}$ in. Early 17th Century. Original Gift (acquired per Drake, 1942), ex Hutton Castle. Inv. No. 374; Reg. No. 45.351.

236 Oval medallion with the shield of CROFTS *(differenced by a crescent)* impaling COTTON *(sable a chevron ermine between three griffins' heads erased argent)* in a cartouche with swags of fruit; yellow stain and enamel; $14\frac{1}{2} \times 9\frac{3}{4}$ in. Early 17th Century. Acquired per Drake, 1948. Inv. No. 487; Reg. No. 45.356.

237 Oval medallion with the shield of EDMUND CROFTS impaling KITSON *(sable three lucies hauriant argent a chief or)* quartering DONNINGTON *(1)* and *(4) paly of six argent and azure on a chief gules three besants; (2) and (3) argent a chevron between three mullets gules)* in a cartouche and laurel wreath (chiefly eroded) with inscribed scroll: Edm Crofts and Kitson; yellow stain and enamel; $16\frac{3}{4} \times 12\frac{1}{2}$ in. Early 17th Century. Original Gift (acquired per Drake, 1942), ex. Hutton Castle. Inv. No. 376; Reg. No. 45.353.

238 Oval medallion with the shield of CROFTS *(differenced by a crescent)* impaling SAMPSON *(argent on a cross patonce gules between four escallops sable a mullet or)* in a cartouche with fruit swags; yellow stain and enamel; $14\frac{1}{4} \times 9\frac{3}{4}$ in. Early 17th Century. Acquired per Drake, 1948. Inv. No. 489; Reg. No. 45.358.

239 Oval medallion with the shield of CROFTS impaling SHELTON *(azure a cross or charged with a mullet for difference)* in a cartouche and laurel wreath with inscribed scroll; yellow stain and enamel; $16\frac{1}{4} \times 12$ in. Early 17th Century. Acquired per Drake, 1948. Inv. No. 488; Reg. No. 45.357.

240 Oval medallion with the shield of DRURY *(argent on a chief vert two pierced mullets or, a label of three points gules)* impaling CROFTS *(differenced with a crescent)* in a cartouche and laurel wreath with inscribed scroll; yellow stain and enamel; $16\frac{1}{2} \times 12\frac{3}{4}$ in. Early 17th Century. Acquired per Drake, 1948. Inv. No. 490; Reg. No. 45.359.

241 Circular garter medallion ensigned by an earl's coronet with the shield of HASTINGS, EARL OF HUNTINGDON, K.G. *(1) Hastings; (2) Herle; (3) Hungerford; (4) Hungerford of Heytesbury; (5) Peverell; (6) Botreaux; (7) Hankford; (8) Cornwall; (9) Cobham; (10) Courtenay; (11) Hussey; (12) Trafford (Botreux); (13) Gernon; (14) Molyns; (15) De Mauley; (16) Percy; (17) Fitzwilliam; (18) Maudynt; (19) Delapool; (20) Plantagenet, Duke of Clarence; (21) Champney; (22) Perrers; (23) Newburgh (Warwick); (24) Montagu; (25) Holland (Woodstock); (26) Monthermer; (27) Wake; (28) Clare; (29) Despencer);* pot metal; abrasion; yellow stain; enamel; $24\frac{1}{2} \times 15\frac{1}{2}$ in. Late 16th Century. Original Gift; ex Drake, 1946. Inv. No. 379; Reg. No. 45.243.

Perhaps for Henry Hastings, 3rd Earl of Huntingdon, who succeeded to the title in 1561 and died without issue in 1595.

242 Circular garter medallion ensigned by an earl's coronet with the shield of TALBOT, EARL OF SHREWSBURY, K.G. *(1) Belesme; (2) Talbot; (3) Talbot, Co. Cornwall (Valetort); (4) Mountford; (5) Valence; (6) Butler; (7) Strange; (8) Hungerford; (9) Furnival; (10) Verdon; (11) Lovetot);* pot metal; abrasion; yellow stain; enamel; 24½ × 15½ in. Late 16th Century. Original Gift; ex Drake, 1946. Inv. No. 380; Reg. No. 45.244.

Perhaps for George Talbot, 6th Earl of Shrewsbury, who succeeded in 1560 and died in 1590.

243 Circular garter medallion ensigned by a coronet with the shield of SIR HENRY CARY, BARON HUNSDON *(1) Cary; (2) Spencer; (3) Beauchamp; (4) replacement; (5) Newburgh (Warwick); (6) Boleyn; (7) replacement; (8) blank; (9) Hoo (Perrers); (10) Butler; (11) Segrave (Burnell); (12) St. Omer (Haversham); (13) Malmain; (14) Newman; (15) Talmage; (16) Hankford);* pot metal; abrasion; yellow stain; enamel; 24½ × 15¼ in. Late 16th Century. Original Gift; ex Drake, 1946. Inv. No. 381; Reg. No. 45.245.

The 5th and 6th quarters are upside down and the 4th, 7th and 8th are extraneous insertions, the missing quarters being for Beaufort, Berkeley and Delisle.

244 Four quarries with the arms of PEYTON *(sable a cross engrailed or and a mullet for difference)* impaling *(a)* BEAUPRE *(argent on a bend azure three crosses crosslet or); (b)* RICH *(gules a chevron between three crosses crosslet or); (c)* PALMER *(azure three fleur de lys argent within a bordure engrailed or quartering Harthull and Mountney); (d)* CLERE *(argent on a fess azure three eagles displayed or)* in cartouches with inscribed scrolls above the shield; yellow stain and enamel; 6 × 5 in. Early 17th Century. Ex Coll: Knowlton Court, Kent. Original Gift; ex Hutton Castle, 1962. Inv. Nos. 133, 127, 145, 135; Reg. Nos. 45.342, 338, 346, 343.

These quarries and nos. 246 and 248 were probably painted for Sir Samuel Peyton of Knowlton Court (near Deal in Kent) where the Church of St. Clement contains several monuments to the family. A 15th Century ancestor, Thomas Peyton, High Sheriff of Cambridgeshire in 1443, 1453 and 1478, married Margaret, daughter of Sir John Bernard, who appears as a kneeling donor with her husband in one of the windows in Long Melford Church, Suffolk. He married secondly, Margaret, daughter and co-heir of Sir Hugh Franceys of Giffards Hall in Wickhambrook (see no. 246 below). By his first marriage Thomas Peyton acquired the Isleham estate in Cambridgeshire, where the church contains a monumental brass to him and his two wives, as well as several 16th century Peyton monuments. The Beaupre, Rich and Clere impalements in no. 244 represent the wives of an uncle, a great uncle and great grandfather of Sir Samuel Peyton of Knowlton. The third quarry is for Sir Christopher Peyton, Kt. of S. Edmund's Bury, Auditor of Ireland, who married Anne, daughter of William Palmer, Esq., of co. Warwick.

**Cat. No. 244 (b)**

245 Shield of TENCH *(argent on a chevron between three lions' heads erased gules a cross crossle or)* impaling FISHER *(azure a fess counter embattled between three dolphins embowed or)*; red pot metal; abrasion; yellow stain; blue enamel; $8 \times 5\frac{1}{2}$ in. 18th Century. Original Gift; ex Hutton Castle, 1962. Inv. No. 141; Reg. No. 45.362.

246 Three Quarries with the arms of PEYTON impaling *(a)* HASELDEN *(argent a cross flory sable)*; *(b)* FRANCIS *(gules a chevron engrailed ermine between three eagles close)*; *(c)* GERNON *(argent three piles wavy gules)*, and one quarry *(d)* with the arms of PIGOTT *(argent three chess rooks sable on a chief of the second a crescent or)* impaling PEYTON; the shields within cartouches bearing inscribed scrolls; yellow stain and enamel; $6 \times 5$ in. Early 17th Century. Ex Coll: Knowlton Court, Kent. Original Gift; ex Hutton Castle, 1962. Inv. Nos. 138, 150, 148, 136; Reg. Nos. 45.345, 349, 348, 344.

The Haselden, Francis and Gernon impalements represent the wives of a great-uncle, a great-great-grandfather (i.e. Thomas Peyton, see note to no. 244) and a still more distant ancestor of Sir Samuel Peyton of Knowlton. Robert Pigott, Esq., of Desart, Ireland, was the second husband of Thomasine Peyton, daughter and co-heir of Sir Christopher Peyton, Kt.

247 Quarry with the shield of VAUGHAN *(sable a chevron between three fleurs de lys argent)* impaling CONWAY *(or a griffin segreant gules)* in a cartouche; yellow stain and enamel; $6 \times 5$ in. Early 17th Century. Original Gift; ex Drake, 1942. Inv. No. 378; Reg. No. 45.354.

248 Four Quarries with the arms of Peyton relatives: *(a)* HALES *(gules three arrows points downward in pale)* impaling PEYTON; *(b)* MONING *(gules three crescents or)* impaling PEYTON; *(c)* JENNE *(ermine a bend cotised gules)* impaling BARNARD *(argent a bear rampant sable collared or)*; *(d)* BROOKE *(gules on a chevron argent a lion rampant sable, a crescent for difference)* impaling ASHFIELD *(sable a fess engrailed between three fleurs de lys argent)*; the shields in cartouches bearing inscribed scrolls; $6 \times 5$ in. Early 17th Century. Ex Coll: Knowlton Court, Kent. Original Gift; ex Hutton Castle, 1962. Inv. Nos. 128, 130, 147, 125; Reg. Nos. 45.339, 341, 347, 337.

Sir Samuel Peyton's sister Anne married Thomas Hales, Esq., eldest son of Sir Charles Christopher Hales, Kt. of Thanington, Kent. His aunt, Elizabeth, married Thomas Moning, Esq., eldest son of John Moning, Lieutenant of Dover Castle. The third quarry is probably a false amalgam of two different shields in the same series. Francis Peyton, Esq. (d. 1529), married a lady of the Brooke family.

249 Shield of PEROTT *(or a boar passant sable)* quartering TRERICE *(sable three chevrons argent);* yellow stain and black enamel; 6×5 in. ? 16th Century. Original Gift; ex Hutton Castle, 1962. Inv. No. 134; Reg. No. 45.149.

The arms of Trerice occur in stained glass at Luccombe (c. 1538) and Selworthy in Somerset.

250 Lozenge shaped shield of PAYNELL *(gules a cross argent)* impaling SEGNY *(gules a cross argent within an orle of martlets or);* yellow stain and enamel; 5×4½ in. 16th Century. Original Gift; ex Hutton Castle, 1962. Inv. No. 97; Reg. No. 45.203.

251 Quarry with the shield of HENRY VANE of Hadlow, and Elizabeth, daughter of Henry WHITE of Christchurch *(dexter: (1) Vane; (2) Creting; (3) George; (4) St. Owen; (5) Fitzellis; (6) Knightley; (7) Gurney; (8) Felton; (9) Frognall; at fess point a crescent for difference; Sinister: White);* yellow stain and enamel; 5×4½ in. Early 17th Century. Original Gift; ex Hutton Castle, 1962. Inv. No. 98; Reg. No. 45.204.

Henry Vane, imprisoned and pardoned for taking part in Sir Thomas Wyatt's insurrection of 1553, became member of Parliament for Winchilsea. He married Elizabeth White, widow of Sir John Godsalve in 1558, and is the ancestor of the 1st Baron Barnard of Barnard Castle and his heirs, the Earls of Darlington and the Dukes of Cleveland. He died in 1580.

252 Panel with helm *(affronty),* mantling, crest *(a wyvern's head charged with a chevron sable)* and shield ensigned by a coronet *(gules a chevron between three martlets sable);* yellow stain and enamel; 6×5 in. Dutch, 17th Century. Original Gift; ex Hutton Castle, 1962. Inv. No. 146, Reg. No. 45.534.

253 Shield *(1) argent two goats rampant sable; (2) gules a bull's head cabossed argent; (3) fragmentary— ? gules two storks argent; (4) argent a goat rampant sable);* enamel; 6×5 in. Dutch, 17th Century. Original Gift; ex Hutton Castle, 1962. Inv. No. 137; Reg. No. 45.533.

254 Panel with helm, mantling, crest *(a lobster gules)* and two shields *(dexter shield: or an eagle dimidiated displayed sable impaling gules a saltire and merchant's mark argent; sinister shield: sable a lobster in pale gules impaling or, a fess between a pelican vulning and three holly leaves vert);* yellow stain and enamel; 6×5 in. Dutch, 17th Century. Original Gift; ex Hutton Castle, 1962. Inv. No. 149; Reg. No. 45.535.

255 Shield *(sable a cross or and in base an estoile argent);* yellow stain and black enamel; 11½×9½ in. Flemish, 16th Century. Original Gift; ex Hutton Castle. Inv. No. 264; Reg. No. 45.465.

256 Roundel with St. Clara of Assisi and a kneeling abbess with shaped shield *(sable an inverted eagle's wing argent and in pale a crozier or);* landscape background with monastery on hill; yellow stain; dia. 10 in. Flemish, early 16th Century. Original Gift; ex Hutton Castle, 1956. Inv. No. 171; Reg. No. 45.446.

257 Shield *(or a stag's head cabossed sable quartering azure an increscent and decrescent moon conjoined or);* pot metal; yellow stain; 10½×9 in. ? Swiss, 16th Century. Original Gift; ex Hutton Castle. Inv. No. 267; Reg. No. 45.500.

258 Shield *(azure in chief a torteau in base a crescent or all within a bordure gules);* pot metal; yellow stain; 8¼×7¼ in. ? Flemish, 16th Century. Original Gift; ex Hutton Castle. Inv. No. 290; Reg. No. 45.468.

259 Roundel with the closed helm, mantling, crest *(a demi-eagle erect sable)* and shaped shield *(per fess in chief or a demi-eagle erect sable and in base a mace head or);* pot metal part green part blue border with inscription including the names of Helen, Menelaus and Paris (Helena . . . Menelai weib . . . Paris geraubt); yellow stain and black enamel; dia. 11 in. German, ? Nuremberg, early 16th Century. Lit: Wentzel, Pantheon XIX (Sept./Oct.), 1961, p. 247. Acquired per Drake, 1947. Inv. No. 438; Reg. No. 45.493.

260 Shield *(quarterly (1) and (4) gules a fleur de lys or; (2) or issuing from a billet raguly a trefoil sable; (3) or a fleur de lys between four billets gules);* yellow stain snd enamel; 9½×7¾ in. ? Dutch, 17th Century. Original Gift; ex Hutton Castle, 1948. Inv. No. 215; Reg. No. 45.539.

261 Panel with the kneeling figures of SIEGFRIED VON GELNHAUSEN and wife with their arms *(dexter shield: per pale argent and gules, an eagle displayed sable and lily argent dimidiated; sinister shield: sable a swan naiant argent)*; pot metal; 22 × 29½ in. German, 1st half 15th Century. From the Carmelite Church, Boppard on Rhine. Ex Coll: Baron Puckler (acquired 1818); Hearst; Robert Goelet of Rhode Island, U.S.A. Lit: Wentzel, Pantheon XIX (Sept./Oct.), 1961, p. 243 (repro.). Original Gift (acquired per Grosvenor Thomas and Drake and stored by them in New York until delivery to Glasgow in 1948. Inv. No. 358; Reg. No. 45.489.

This panel formed the lowest part of a lancet window depicting the Madonna and one of the Ten Commandments from Boppard, but although also from the same church it did not originally belong to this window and has now been extracted. The dexter shield with the half eagle impaling the half lily has been identified by Professor Hans Wentzel of Stuttgart as that of Siegfried von Gelnhausen since the above cited article was published.

262 Panel with a Swiss soldier bearing a banner with the arms of ZUG *(argent a fess azure in dexter chief a canton or with the Mater Dolorosa)*; on the right is the shield of Zug surmounted by the crowned shield of the Empire *(or a two-headed eagle displayed sable, crowned and nimbed or)*; above are St. Michael and St. Oswald; below is written: Die Statt Zug, 1605; pot metal; yellow stain; enamel; 13¼ × 9¼ in. Swiss, early 17th Century. Acquired per Drake, 1946. Inv. No. 436; Reg. No. 45.510.

263 Roundel with the arms of ZUG comprising two shields *(argent a fess azure)* with lion supporters *(plumed and helmed)* surmounted by the arms of the Empire; below are six shields conjoined for Walschwil *(azure a tree vert)*; Steinhusen *(argent a steinbock rampant sable)*; Rham *(argent a bear rampant gules)*; Hunenberg *(azure two turkeys' heads addorsed)*; Gangetschwil *(or a goat and tree)*; Ruti *(or a crown of thorns ? sable)*; inscribed: Die Statt Zug, 1668; yellow stain and blue, red and black enamel; dia. 6 in. Swiss, 17th Century. Original Gift; ex Hutton Castle, 1962. Inv. No. 132; Reg. No. 45.512.

264 Panel depicting the interior of a metal foundry with two shaped shields *(dexter shield: azure charged with a bell argent; sinister shield: fragmentary)* between inscribed names: Vettes Fussto (?) on the dexter and Elspeth Schalk (?) 1550 on the sinister; above are two vignettes of a shooting range and a cannon; red pot metal; yellow stain; blue and black enamel; 14½ × 9 in. Swiss, 16th Century. Original Gift; ex Hutton Castle. Inv. No. 324; Reg. No. 45.503.

265 Roundel with the arms of JACOB and MARGARETTA HACHT comprising helm *(closed, steel, affronty)*, mantling *(dexter gules doubled argent; sinister gules doubled or)*, crest *(a demi-figure vested gules bearing in dexter hand three ostrich plumes or, gules and argent)*, and two shields *(dexter shield: gules two ostrich plumes in saltire or and argent; sinister shield: per bend argent and or three bends sinister gules and a steinbock sable rampant)*; blue border inscribed : 1531 Jacob von Hacht and Margaretta sein eeliche hausfrau; red and blue pot metal; abrasion; yellow stain; dia. 12¼ in. Swiss, 16th Century. Acquired per Drake, 1946.   Inv. No. 434; Reg. No. 45.508.

266 Panel with two achievements for THEOBALDUS SCHWENDT and his wife below six mourners (father, mother, daughter and three sons) grouped around a coffin *(dexter shield supported by an angel: or a rose tree growing out of a heart; sinister shield: per fess argent and sable two demi-horses counter-changed);* on either side are the figures of Faith and Hope and above is a depiction of the Last Judgment; the dexter achievement is inscribed: Theobaldus Schwendt, AEtatis suae . . . . . ; the sinister: Barbara Acke . . . n sein hausfrau Aetatis suae 56; between the escutcheons is a quotation from II Timothy, chap. 4, v. 7 and 8; red pot metal; abrasion; yellow stain; blue and black enamel; 14½ × 12½ in. Swiss, 17th Century. Original Gift; ex Hutton Castle.   Inv. No. 326; Reg. No. 45.524.

267 Roundel with unidentified armorial achievement comprising closed helm, mantling *(or doubled sable)*, crest *(male torso of the shield issuing from a coronet)* and shaped shield *(or a crowned male torso habited sable);* above is a land and seascape abraded in blue; blue pot metal; abrasion; yellow stain; black enamel; dia. 12¾ in. Swiss, 16th Century. Acquired per Drake, 1946.   Inv. No. 437; Reg. No. 45.511.

268 Panel with the shield of WETTINGEN *(azure two garbs in saltire or)* below a depiction of Joachim and St Anne with the Virgin and Child; inscribed below: Gottes Gnaden Hus Wettingen Seckelmeyster 1593; and above are five pious lines in praise of St. Anne beginning Anna du dienerin gottes; red pot metal; abrasion; yellow stain; blue enamel; 12½ × 8½ in. Swiss, late 16th Century. Original Gift; ex Hutton Castle.   Inv. No. 323; Reg. No. 45.502.

269 Panel with the armorial achievement of a bishop flanked by St Gall and St Othmar, the shield *(quarterly: (1) or a bear rampant sable; (2) azure a Paschal Lamb argent; (3) argent a cock sable crowned with thorns holding grapes; (4) or a hound sable collared or)* surmounted by a jewelled mitre and two croziers; yellow stain; blue and black enamel; 8¼ × 10½ in. Swiss, 17th Century. Original Gift; ex Hutton Castle, 1948.   Inv. No. 235; Reg. No. 45.518.

270 Panel with a representation of the Madonna and Child between an armorial achievement comprising shaped shield *(gules a cross throughout or, ? sic for argent)* surmounted by helm, coronet and crest *(a demi-vol charged with a cross of the field)* and the shield of OSWALD EISNER *(argent three mountain peaks azure)*; above is the date 1550 inscribed on a cartouche between a depiction of the Baptism and the figure of St. John Evangelist; below is the inscription: FRATER OSWALD EISENER ORDINIS SANCTI IOHANNIS BAPTISTI; red and blue pot metal; abrasion; yellow stain; 13¼ × 9½ in. Swiss, mid 16th Century. Original Gift; ex Hutton Castle. Inv. No. 366; Reg. No. 45.506.

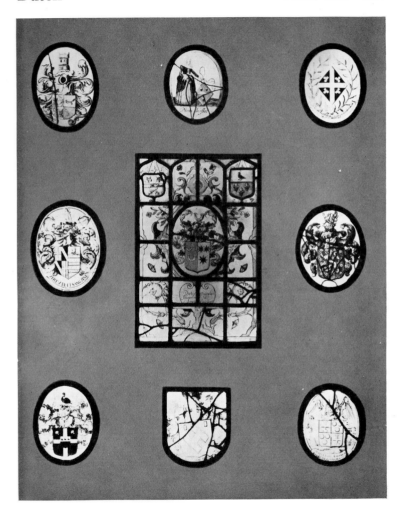

271 Oval medallion with a lady facing half right standing in a landscape with lozenge shaped shield *(argent a double-headed eagle displayed sable)*; enclosed by a yellow stain horseshoe border; inscribed at the foot: Geghewen al Bowen, 1637; yellow stain and enamel; 12⅞ × 9½ in. Dutch, 17th Century. Original Gift; ex Hutton Castle, 1948. Inv. No. 237; Reg. No. 45.548.

272 Oval medallion with armorial achievement comprising helm, mantling, crest *(two wings erect argent and or)* and shield *(per pale: (1) or a pallet couped and in fess dexter a wheel; (2) argent an angel standing in a meadow)*; yellow stain and enamel; 10¼ × 8¾ in. Dutch, 17th Century. Ex Hutton Castle, 1960. Inv. No. 581; Reg. No. 45.578.

273 Oval medallion with a lady facing half left standing in a landscape with lozenge shaped shield for SICKINGHA *(per pale or and argent a double-headed eagle displayed dimidiated per pale sable and gules and debruised on the sinister side by a fess gules)*; enclosed by a yellow stain horse-shoe border; inscribed at the foot: Sa Juffr. Anna van Sickingha vrou van Cammingha, 1638; yellow stain and enamel; 12½ × 9½ in. Dutch, 17th Century. Original Gift; ex Hutton Castle, 1948. Inv. No. 338; Reg. No. 45.549.

274 Oval medallion with armorial achievement of PIETER WOLVERISS VAN LEEVEN comprising helm, mantling, crest *(out of a coronet a lion rampant of the shield)* and shield *(or a lion rampant gules debruised by a label of three points between five billets azure)*; inscribed at the foot with name as above and date: Anno 1637; yellow stain and enamel; 9½ × 8¼ in. Dutch, 17th Century. Original Gift; ex Hutton Castle, 1948. Inv. No. 232; Reg. No. 45.546.

275 Panel with the armorial achievement of WILLEM CLAESSOON VAN OUTSHOOVEN comprising helm, mantling *(gules doubled argent)*, crest *(two wings erect argent and gules, the latter charged with a powder horn)* and shield *(gules three powder horns proper impaling argent three estoiles sable)* within an octagonal cartouche embellished with floral decoration above another cartouche containing an inscription with name and date 1631, the dexter and sinister sides of the shield being repeated in two separate shields at the top; yellow stain and enamel; 23 × 17 in. Dutch, 17th Century. Original Gift; ex Hutton Castle. Inv. No. 312; Reg. No. 45.552.

276 Oval medallion with armorial achievement comprising helm, mantling *(or doubled sable)*, crest *(two wings erect and an acorn)* and shield *(or on a fess sable between five acorns a crescent)*; yellow stain and black enamel; 9¾ × 8 in. Dutch, 17th Century. Ex Hutton Castle, 1960. Inv. No. 579. Reg. No. 45.576.

277 Oval medallion with helm, mantling *(sable doubled argent)*, crest *(demi-boar erect with acorn sprig)* and two shields, the sinister shield being a lozenge, conjoined by tassels *(dexter shield: per fess argent and gules, a boar courant with acorn sprig and a well head or; sinister shield: sable a turnip argent quartering or, three fleurs de lys; on an inescutcheon a swan naiant)*; yellow stain and black enamel; 11 × 8¼ in. Dutch, ? 19th Century. Original Gift; ex Hutton Castle, 1948. Inv. No. 234; Reg. No. 45.560

278 Oval medallion with armorial achievement comprising helm, mantling *(or doubled gules)*, crest *(a split pomegranate)* and shield *(gules, three split pomegranates or enclosed by a crowned serpent impaling azure a harrow or)*; yellow stain; blue and black enamel; 10¾ × 7¾ in. Dutch, 17th Century. Ex Hutton Castle, 1960. Inv. No. 580; Reg. No. 45.577.

279 Oval medallion with armorial achievement comprising helm, mantling, crest *(a cone issuing from a coronet surmounted by bearded man's head)* and shield *(gules five lozenges in cross argent between fifteen billets and in dexter chief a canton vert charged with a fess ermine)*; dated at foot: Ao 1636; yellow stain and enamel; 11 × 9 in. Dutch, 17th Century. Original Gift; ex Hutton Castle, 1948. Inv. No. 233; Reg. No. 45.547.

280 Oval medallion with an armorial achievement comprising helm, mantling, crest *(a castle keep)*, and shield *(per pale: dexter: argent a castle keep quartering a lion rampant; sinister: per fess argent and or (? gules) two stalks of barley in saltire)*; yellow stain and enamel; 10½ × 8 in. Dutch, 17th Century. Ex Hutton Castle, 1960. Inv. No. 570; Reg. No. 45.567.

281 Oval medallion with a widow holding the lozenge shield of MARIA AKERSLOOT *(gules a fish naiant argent between three acorns proper)* enclosed by a grey horse-shoe border; inscribed at foot with name and date 1653; yellow stain and enamel; 9⅛ × 7½ in. Dutch, 17th Century. Ex Hutton Castle, 1960. Inv. No. 583; Reg. No. 45.580.

282 Oval medallion with lozenge shield *(sable a cross throughout or between four trefoils)* set within two green branches above inscribed scroll: Di Godt heeft di heeft al en sonder hem is nit metal; yellow stain and enamel; 9½ × 7½ in. Dutch, 17th Century. Original Gift; ex Hutton Castle, 1948. Inv. No. 228; Reg. No. 45.543.

283 Oval medallion with armorial achievement comprising helm, mantling *(argent doubled gules)*, crest *(a lion's head erased argent crowned or differenced with a crescent)* and shield *(per pale: dexter: gules a cross throughout argent between four swords erect of the second pommelled or quartering sable a bend ermine; sinister: ermine three bars gules, in chief a demi-lion rampant gules)*; in base the motto: Virtute et Sanguine; yellow stain; red and black enamel; 11 × 8¾ in. Dutch, 17th Century. Ex Hutton Castle, 1960 Inv. No. 576; Reg. No. 45.573.

These are probably the arms of an English family, the dexter side being Philpot quartering Philpot.

284 Panel with armorial achievement of PIETER VRANCKEN and ANNETA CORNELIS comprising helm, mantling, crest *(a powder horn)* and shield *(as for Willem Claessoon in No. 275)* within a central oval; top two smaller shields *(dexter shield: or a fess azure between two ox heads in chief and two swords in saltire in base; sinister shield: per fess argent a crow sable and or three fleurs de lys;* inscribed: Pieter Vrancken/ Schaipenbram met/Anneta Cornelis Dr; yellow stain and enamel; 23¾ × 17 in. Dutch, 17th Century. Original Gift; ex Hutton Castle. Inv. No. 314; Reg. No. 45.553.

The two shields in top dexter and sinister seem extraneous insertions.

285 Oval medallion with armorial achievement comprising helm, mantling, crest *(out of a coronet a crowned demi-lion rampant argent and a wing erect gules semy of cinquefoils argent)* and shield *(gules semy of cinquefoils argent a crowned lion rampant argent);* yellow stain and enamel; 10×8 in. Dutch, 17th Century. Ex Hutton Castle, 1960. Inv. No. 578; Reg. No. 45.575.

286 Oval medallion with armorial achievement comprising helm, mantling *(sable doubled or)*, crest *(a martlet sable)* and shield *(sable a cross and in chief two mallets or; on an inescutcheon sable a chief argent charged with three martlets of the field);* yellow stain and black enamel; 9½×7¼ in. Dutch, 17th Century. Ex Hutton Castle, 1960. Inv. No. 577; Reg. No. 45.574.

287 Shield bearing an armorial achievement comprising helm, mantling *(sable doubled argent)*, crest *(two wings erect sable charged with an estoile or)* and shield *(gules five lozenges in cross argent and in chief two billets or);* in base an incomplete inscription: Goeder Ionst Coem Ic . . . . ; yellow stain and black enamel; 9×8 in. Dutch, 17th Century. Original Gift; ex Hutton Castle, 1948. Inv. No. 212; Reg. No. 45.536.

288 Oval medallion with shield of MARIA VAN AMSTEN and ROYDE BEGYNKEN supported by an angel *(gules a cross moline argent quartering argent three torteaux);* in base the inscribed names and date Ao165.; yellow stain and enamel; 9¼×7½ in. Dutch, 17th Century. Original Gift; ex Hutton Castle, 1948. Inv. No. 229; Reg. No. 45.544.

289 Oval shield *(dexter: argent a bull's head cabossed with two crows perched on its horns and a third crow in base; sinister: per fess or three objects (krauwels) sable and gules three roses or seeded and barbed argent);* yellow stain and enamel; 8½×6¾ in. Dutch, 17th Century. Ex Hutton Castle, 1960. Inv. No. 568; Reg. No. 45.565.
The dexter arms may be for van Rijthoven.

290 Panel with armorial achievement comprising helm, mantling, crest *(two wings erect)* and shield *(per pale: dexter: per fess argent a chess rook sable between three fleurs de lys gules and argent a stag trippant; sinister: gules two bars argent between in chief or a castle and in base gules three roses argent seeded or);* red pot metal; abrasion; yellow stain; enamel; 22×14⅛ in. Dutch, 17th Century. Original Gift; ex Hutton Castle, Inv. No. 372; Reg. No. 45.562.

291 Oval medallion with shield of DESPENCER *(quarterly argent and gules a fret or, overall on a bend sable three escallops of the first)* impaling WILSON *(sable a wolf salient charged with a martlet and in chief three mullets or)* in a cartouche; yellow stain; blue, red and black enamel; 8½×6½ in. English, 17th Century. Ex Hutton Castle, 1960. Inv. No. 569; Reg. No. 45.566.

292 Panel with the armorial achievement of JOHAN VAN ZUTPHEN and his wife BELYA VAN DER GAF comprising helm *(steel, garnished or, affronty, with five bars)*, mantling *(gules doubled or)*, crest *(a cone issuing from a coronet surmounted by a rose gules seeded and barbed or)* and shield *(dexter: or three roses gules quartering gules on three pallets ten potents argent and in chief or three mallets sable; sinister: azure a dove of peace argent);* in base a cartouche inscribed: Johan van Zutphen out Schepen en Raet der Stadt Shertogenbosch En Joffrouwe Belya van der Gaf Zyn huys vrouw 1671; red pot metal; abrasion; yellow stain; black and blue enamel; 21¾×12 in. Dutch, late 17th Century. Original Gift; ex Hutton Castle. Inv. No. 369; Reg. No. 45.558.

293 Oval medallion with winged stag supporting a shield *(argent three belt buckles impaling argent two wings conjoined erect)* within a yellow cartouche and the date: 1(6)11; yellow stain and black enamel; 6¼×4⅞ in. ? English, early 17th Century. Original Gift; ex Hutton Castle. Inv. No. 286; Reg. No. 45.231.

294 Panel with the armorial achievement of FREDERICK TOURAILLON DE MASSIN and his wife LEVINA DE VRIES comprising helm *(steel garnished or, affronty with five bars)*, mantling *(gules doubled or)*, crest *(a demi-griffin rampant or)* and shield *(per pale: dexter: gules three demi-griffins rampant or; sinister: argent a mill-wheel gules quartering or five lozenges sable three and two);* in base a cartouche inscribed: Jor Frederick Touraillon de Massin En Joffn Levina de Vries syn huiysvrou Ao 1671; yellow stain; red and black enamel; 22×11¾ in. Dutch, late 17th Century. Original Gift; ex Hutton Castle. Inv. No. 370; Reg. No. 45.559.

295 Oval medallion with armorial achievement comprising helm, mantling, crest *(an estoile or)*, and shield *(a seascape with three-masted, ten-gun battleship in full sail with a red, white and blue flag at the prow; in chief dexter and sinister two estoiles or);* yellow stain and enamel; 8½×6½ in. Dutch, 17th Century. Original Gift; ex Hutton Castle. Inv. No. 365; Reg. No. 45.557.

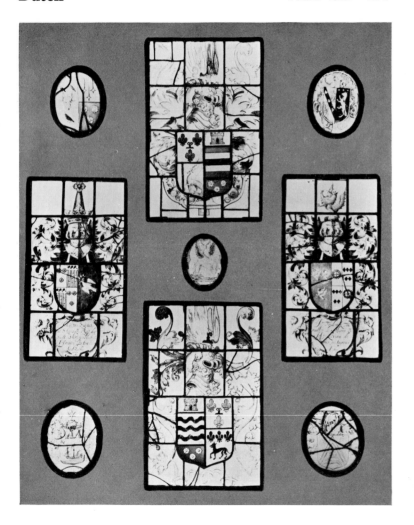

296 Panel with armorial achievement comprising helm, mantling, crest *(a chess rook sable between two wings erect)* and shield *(dexter: as for sinister side of No. 290 but or three bars wavy sable; sinister: per fess argent a chess rook sable between three fleurs de lys gules and argent a bear cub trippant and in chief three fleurs de lys sable)*; red pot metal; abrasion; yellow stain; enamel; $21\frac{7}{8} \times 14\frac{3}{4}$ in. Dutch, 17th Century. Original Gift; ex Hutton Castle. Inv. No. 373; Reg. No. 45.563.

297 Oval medallion with helm, mantling and shield *(or a chevron between three roses and in base a hound courant argent)*; yellow stain; $8\frac{1}{2} \times 7$ in. Dutch, 17th Century. Ex Hutton Castle, 1960. Inv. No. 572; Reg. No. 45.569.

298 Oval medallion with the ROYAL (TUDOR) ARMS OF ENGLAND *(France and England quarterly)*; wreath border with roses top and sides; pot metal; abrasion; yellow stain; $17 \times 12$ in. English, 16th Century. Ex Coll: Vale Royal (Entrance Hall, east window). Lit: The Genealogist, XXXVIII, 1921-2, 44. Acquired per Drake, 1947. Inv. No. 445; Reg. No. 45.254. See no. 156.

299 Roundel with two incidents in the life of a saint and in base the armorial achievement of WOLFGANG KEISER and his wife MARIA MAGDALENA SCHLUMPFIN comprising helm *(azure, garnished or, affronty with five bars)*, mantling *(gules doubled or)*, crest *(a demi-male figure vested sable charged with a cross or and holding two estoiles in his outstretched arms)* and two shields *(dexter: sable the letter T between two estoiles or; sinister: gules the letter V and a cross argent)*; inscribed: Herr Wolfgang Keiser des Raths alt Seckelmeister der Statt und ambt Zug Fr. Maria Magdalena Schlumpfin sein Ehe gemacht 1671; yellow stain and enamel; dia. $7\frac{3}{8}$ in. Swiss, late 17th Century. Original Gift; ex Hutton Castle. Inv. No. 368; Reg. No. 45.530.

300 Oval medallion ensigned by a red rose with the arms of EDWARD, PRINCE OF WALES, afterwards Edward VI *(France and England quarterly with a label of three points argent)*; pot metal; abrasion; yellow stain; $17 \times 12$ in. English, 16th Century. Ex Coll: Vale Royal (but not listed in The Genealogist, XXXVIII, 1921-2). Acquired per Drake, 1947. Inv. No. 450; Reg. No. 45.259.

301 Roundel with the shaped shield of ARDERN *(gules three crosses botonny fitchy or and a chief of the last)* within a wreath border; pot metal; yellow stain; dia. 18¾ in. English, 16th Century. Acquired per Drake, 1948. Inv. No. 484, Reg. No. 45.289.

These arms, with the addition of a martlet on the chief, are those granted to John Shakespeare (father of William) who married the daughter and heir of Robert Ardern of Wellingcote.

302 Panel depicting King Edward I as Prince of Wales at sea in a storm vowing to the Virgin that he would found a monastery at Vale Royal if he survived shipwreck; at the stern of the boat a pennant with the ROYAL ARMS *(gules three lions or)*; inscribed: Rex Edouardus post conq. primus in periculo maris votu(m) facit de Coenob. fundand in honore B.V.M.; red pot metal; abrasion; yellow stain; enamel; 21¾ × 16¼ in. English, c. 1800. Ex Coll: Vale Royal (Saloon, east window). Lit: The Genealogist, XXXVIII, 1921-2, p. 5. Acquired per Drake, 1947. Inv. No. 478; Reg. No. 45.103.

The mansion of Vale Royal was built after 1542 on the site of the monastery by Sir Thomas Holcroft. In 1616 it was acquired by the Cholmondeleys whose descendant is Lord Delamere, the present owner. See nos. 154 et seq. This and the following panel are believed to be copies of a medieval illumination or fresco.

303 Panel depicting Edward I enthroned granting to the first abbot of Vale Royal, John Champneys, the promised monastery; in the window on the right are the Royal Arms of England and in the window on the left are the arms of VALE ROYAL *(gules three lions of England debruised by a crozier in pale)*; inscribed: Rex Edouardus post conqu. primus Coenobiu statuit apud Valle Regale in honore B.V.M.; red pot metal; abrasion; yellow stain; enamel; 21 × 16 in. English, c. 1800. Ex Coll: Vale Royal (Saloon, west window). Lit: The Genealogist, XXXVIII, 1921-2, 5. Acquired per Drake, 1947. Inv. No. 479; Reg. No. 45.104.

Cat. No. 203

Cat. No. 225

# INDEX

including blazons of quarterings not given in the catalogue.